NOTES ON THE SONNETS

Luke Kennard is the author of five collections of poetry and three pamphlets. His second collection, *The Harbour Beyond the Movie*, was shortlisted for the 2007 Forward Prize for Best Collection and his fifth, *Cain*, for the 2017 Dylan Thomas Prize. He lectures in Creative Writing at the University of Birmingham.

ALSO BY LUKE KENNARD

POETRY

The Solex Brothers (Stride, 2005)
The Harbour Beyond the Movie (Salt, 2007)
The Migraine Hotel (Salt, 2009)
Planet-shaped Horse (Nine Arches, 2011)
The Necropolis Boat (Holdfire, 2012)
A Lost Expression (Salt, 2013)
Cain (Penned in the Margins, 2016)
Truffle Hound (Verve, 2018)
Mise en Abyme (Tungsten, 2019)

FICTION

Holophin (Penned in the Margins, 2012)
The Transition (Fourth Estate, 2017)

Notes on the Sonnets

LUKE KENNARD

Penned in the Margins

LONDON

PUBLISHED BY PENNED IN THE MARGINS
Toynbee Studios, 28 Commercial Street, London E1 6AB
www.pennedinthemargins.co.uk

First published 2021

Printed in the United Kingdom by TJ Books Limited

ISBN
978-1-908058-81-2

All of this takes place at the same house party. The order of the sonnets is determined by events. They are to be seen as improvisations, or annotations, or variations.

Notes
on the
Sonnets

I

Sometimes a party feels like a portal you have to pass through, sometimes not. I don't know with cocaine. It's like everyone cheating on the same cryptic crossword (9). My ideal recreational drug would be a pill that makes people feel more insecure and I'm the only one at the party not taking it. I'm in the kitchen with a man who says he can recite any of Shakespeare's sonnets if someone gives him a number from 1 to 154. And I'm like, Wow, that's great. 66? And he says, no. Not 66. Anything but that. I'm like, Okay, hahaha, you're full of shit. He says, I'm not lying, I'm just not reciting sonnet 66, tonight or any other night. I hate it. This has honestly never happened to me before. Give me any other number. And I find that hard to believe, because if you're asked to pick a random number from 1 to 154 the chances are it might be 66. But I sip from the rum and Coke someone gave me and I sigh and I say, okay, 102. And he starts, I swear this is a true story, he starts cold, *My love is strenghten'd though more weak in seeming...* I turn on the convection hob and put my palm on it.

You give me the private signal to rescue you and I have to interrupt you kissing an artist on the staircase. I can tell that she is an artist because she is so covered in paint and so, now, are you. The way construction workers are always building things, the way demolition crews never really get to take a day off: the demolition never ends, they take it with them when they go. What's our excuse? A writer is always looking for creative ways to fall into a threshing machine. You're all, Woah, who invited the oncologist. We're talking to an award-winning double-act. Do you get tired, we ask them, of being a double-act? Do people expect you still to be a double-act when you're off-duty? But they say it's okay because their act is based on the fact that they have no natural repartee. You have to do something which destroys you, some personal brand which subdues your nature: everybody knows that. What you draw out with one undefiant glance. Oh, you. O, you. I know. We will give each other a disease to which we alone are the cure, the cure that reinfects, the reinfection that's the cure.

We have been told that the perfect human is at the party. We look forward to meeting them and finding out what they're like. Unassailable. Beyond reproach. Naturally there are rumours of their misdeeds. The perfect human is not perfect; this assumption reflects badly on us. Yes, the perfect human has done some pretty bad shit, but they've also been through a lot. They came from humble origins, but now they write celebrated papers demythologising the "humble origins" trope. They keep their money in a dirty pillowcase and distribute it generously. They don't really *like* the one art for which they are recognised or the field in which they incontestably dominate; they prefer NASCAR. They say this in interviews a lot. There is not a single act of cruelty, selfishness and abuse of power the perfect human has committed which cannot be fully explained by systemic issues they themselves have gracefully endured and emerged triumphant. This is what we mean when we say the perfect human does not exist: we mean they are like Euler's Identity equation. An equation so beautiful it has been compared to a Shakespearean sonnet. Five complex numbers are plotted on the complex plane and together form a "house shape." When we meet them we will say that we are big fans. Big fans, the perfect human will say. My father worked in a factory that made big fans. *But look at you now, perfect human*, we will say, *look at you now.*

I rarely think of my son when I'm at a party, and then I remember something he said last night before falling asleep on my arm and it floors me. Maybe just come with me. This is me in the hallway talking to someone I don't really like and the effort hurts my jaw due to the build-up of lactic acid. Maybe not. The room is blood-temperature. As if I could wake up with an ashtray mouth and find that I dreamed the last 7 years in a single night. If I thought about *him* it would be as if I'd brought him with me and I want to stress that it's not him I'd be embarrassed about or even my own self-consciousness. I once bought bright red shoes and immediately regretted it. I brought my kid with me – can you believe that? It's the people who'd say *Why is there a seven-year-old at this party?* I wouldn't want their paucity of spirit / adaptation so exposed. Choose what you give yourself to, beautiful boy. It happens that I've seen exactly forty winters, even if that's just a code for "lots". I remember confronting you about the six empty boxes of Jaffa Cakes under your bed and you wondered why I'd assume you had anything to do with it. Oh babe, my apology for absence, mon semblable, my old excuse.

Without meaning to we're taking photos of each other taking photos of each other again. We're outside the kitchen window getting high around a tin table until all I can talk about is a Rubik's cube where every face is made of another smaller Rubik's cube, but it would only work if they're spheres. Then I get quite agitated and demand someone fetches me the pepper grinder because of the terpenoids, and I like the way the word feels in my mouth so much I just keep saying it, *terpenoids terpenoids terpenoids*. Unblessed in the evening air, unblessed. There's such an obsession with wrinkles in sonnets 1-74 it's as if the whole sequence had been commissioned by a luxury skin care salve. I don't know about you, but I didn't have children so that they'd *look* like me; it feels weird even having to point that out. Although, you say, head cocked, reflected in the window I just photographed the people photographing themselves through, it's actually quite important being pretty, isn't it? More than we care to admit? I like having attractive friends. I laugh because you do. That's a low-key outrageous thing to say. No it's not. Anyway, everyone's attractive. There is a warmth in just leaning against the windowsill with you I'll come back to. I would like you to lie on top of me in a pile of coats. I would like you to hold me and knock insistently on the top of my head. I would like you to bask in the good thoughts I have about you.

I think I told you about my friend who, when we were 17, had a date tattooed on his ankle and to my shame I can't remember the exact date – *XX.05.25* – because our idea was that we should all meet up in exactly 25 years' time on Hamm Hill, surrounded by living flowers, whatever else was going on in our lives, whatever we'd done, whatever had been done to us, whatever, just drive over there from wherever we'd washed up, drawn by our own sweet skill or otherwise, and meet up at precisely 6pm on that day. But the consensus was that we'd probably only remember it if we got the date tattooed on our ankles; we didn't think it possible to remember Happy Hour in the perfectly dingy Bell and Crown a whole 25 years later although, of course, I do. And he was the sweetest and most impulsive and he went ahead and got the tattoo the next week and we were like… Oh god, you took that seriously? 25 years seemed like a comically long time to us. He was justifiably angry – we'd agreed! It was a pact! We were all, No! It was hypothetical and also tattoos sound really painful. That's endearing and also really awful, you say. You check my bare ankle to be sure it wasn't me.

From now on I am going to audit this party which means I will be present but not in the capacity of consuming anything or actively engaging with anyone. It's like one of the more inscrutable parables / brutal parallels: the master gives one talent each to three servants. I've just checked and it turns out that one talent is 33kg of silver, which is worth *loads*. Anyway, one of them invests it; one of them really goes to town on it, hedge bets it or something like the first recorded disaster capitalist and, hey, makes a killing; but the third servant... he just literally *buries* it in the ground like a fucking idiot and mumbles something about knowing the master to be a ruthless man so he wanted to make sure nothing happened to the talent. The master is not impressed by this at all. That other secret chord which David played and the Lord *hated* it. Telling someone they're too hard on themselves is the kindest thing you can say to anyone; *you are a rare, self-sabotaging tree. How have you even grown in this crummy environment?* Also, probably, it's true and they may have some useful pointers. The day will come when they will throw us out of the temple and believe they are serving God and the devil will say, It's got a little complicated.

I would also like my skin to be thought, but it isn't. I have to carry it places, whereas thoughts have wings. A sub-party has started in the porch. We all have teleportation fantasies, but the quantum channel is always destroyed. So you could do it once and never come back. In such a way, in wishing it were otherwise, all science-fiction corresponds to our desire to renounce all responsibility for our actions. Crime fiction our desire to delegate. Criminality is bureaucracy in its purest uncut form. There is, though, some distant molecule forever altered, though you wouldn't know it, turning up on your doorstep like an unsolicited submission. A drastic, last-ditch signal. So you can go back once and try again but do exactly the same things differently and exactly the same things the same because you already went back. Teleport to the last ditch. The ribbons above the window say *Distraction is Perfidy*. If the dull substance of my thoughts were *skin* we'd walk along the skin-lined thoroughfare and pause under a fleshy, pulsating tree, I'd say, In all this hideous world you found me.

Moiety: two parts. Taxation. In property law, for instance, you own half your maisonette and lease the other half from someone else. The moiety in your brother's eye. Some molecules are water-loving. Some molecules are water-fearing. In anthropology moiety means one of two distinct groups within a tribe.

I interned for three years as an interloper and now I care about things which should not concern me, broke the key off in the lock, spent the deposit. Here are the two parts of your country, here are the two distinct tribes within each half, here are... In French it just means *half*. In theology you own one of your eyes and the other belongs to God.

A bible study group is meeting in the dusty space between the landing and the bathroom. Something bad must have happened at the party so people have fallen back on old habits. Sometimes you end up dating someone who attends a Pentecostal church where 1. There are doughnuts afterwards and 2. They speak in tongues for upwards of an hour during the services. If you're like me you'd go along with it up to the speaking in tongues; if you're like me, you'd draw the line at that because it's presumptuous to think the Holy Spirit is being poured out upon you. So it was a relief to find prayers which had been through a rigorous peer-review process; which you are to commit to memory and speak over and over again. This is where the traditional Protestant line would take against the superstition of something too close to a spell, a riddle, an incantation; that they served us pretty well for seventeen centuries notwithstanding. This is me bedecked with swallows drawn to me solely by my indefatigable inner peace. This is me consuming the very substance of my soul due to what experts call "tinderbox conditions". And really, what would you say to God, given absolute carte blanche? *God... Um...* But what I mean is, I do not expect you to mean it when you say *I love you*, which you do more frequently when you don't, because we are junctions. I have loved you, I will love you, my love for you is in a permanent state of departure and arrival.

To unlook. I unlook for you. I try to attain a permanent state of unlooking. Ideally, you're not with me. You're in another room and people are admiring you. Someone has spilled wine on your dress. You are crouching on the floor by a decommissioned soldier. He has both his hands in yours and you are saying, *I'm so sorry*. People do not carry their awards with them, even if they should, especially to parties; Most Compassionate 1992. People with honours are not happy, but not because they fear the honours might be taken away or even because they feel guilty about the honours. It's something else. 'Did I really die for this?' [Gestures vaguely at the party.] 'Yes. And we're not grateful.' Does the warrior really fear being forgotten? I don't know. Posterity is like a cat that thinks it's Jesus: we wouldn't even know. You don't get this at all, but I love it when someone else has a crush on you. Something that never existed in the first place cannot be estranged. Better to marry than to burn, but both can be arranged.

The way hangovers mature, in your 30s, into a kind of existential mould. I want the kind of success and happiness for you I want for my own children. I want you to feel loved and known or known and loved or, failing that, because really who can expect such extravagance, I want the ache to be transfigured into something you can use. Otherwise, knowing that you exist, that at this moment you are waiting for a train, that you have had to start the same page again because you weren't concentrating, that you are tired, that if someone asked you something they would get to hear your voice. I love the channels dammed with exhausting half-thoughts. Funny how the latte has become one of the laziest class signifiers, as if every dead high-street didn't contain at least two Costas.

The mathematician draws sequences of *w*s and *m*s in the condensation on the window. Every interval contains infinite transcendental numbers. Okay? Yes, I say, I'm genuinely interested. Do you want to draw the next one? *m w m w w m w w w…* No, she says, That's too many ws. She draws another sequence. This sequence cannot occur anywhere in the infinite list of sequences, even though it's infinite. Do you understand? No, I tell her, I'm an Intuitionist. Each muse is responsible for two muses who are in turn responsible for two muses who are responsible for two muses. Zoom out far enough and it looks like a flower, further and it just looks like the world. Look you *did* ask, she says, clearing the window with her sleeve. I was having a nice night. Take this party, I say. It remains forever in the status of creation, but is not a closed realm of things existing in themselves. Actual infinity was taken as a threat to the absolute infinity of God. At one point Georg Cantor sent a letter directly to Pope Leo XIII to clarify. All infinities are at the disposal of the Almighty. Cantor's youngest son died in 1899 while Cantor was in the middle of giving a lecture on Baconian theory and Shakespeare. Shakespeare's only son died aged 11 in 1596. Is it mindless sentimentality to feel sad about this? What is that feeling? The universe, if real, must be *finite* – she grabs one of my earlobes and squeezes, hard – in both space and time. You're hurting me. The essence of mathematics is its *freedom*. She lets go of my ear. No-one shall expel us from the paradise it has created.

So that there's no uncertainty on the matter. So there's a guy standing on the sofa, and a sofa is not an easy surface to stand on, and he's reading out everything he's ever written, from secondary school English Lit A-level coursework onwards. So we'll be here all night. So easy to sneer at this, but just as easy to grab a beanbag, close your eyes and chart the gradual evolution of his style. So what's required of us, when we find someone embarrassing, is to love them. So far beyond caring what any of you think of me where once I had – it's unimprovable – an adder's sense. So now it's only you I can let down. So that's that. So I am not read as neutral I have taken to exaggerating that which I can control, which is my scarf. So many more important things, so many dog-eared pages, so what. So everybody here died long ago, or soon they will. So give me your best guess, another drink, your disapproval, your disappearing act. So I know.

The bridge. The mountain. The lake. The ibex. The chocolate cake. *The Collected Poems of Robert Lowell.* The jar of cinnamon sticks. The slapping rain. The tiny dog. The paint chipped from the windowsill. The momentary concerned glance which passes like a shaft of light. The coffee cup. The flooded rails. The empty cracked shell of a snail. The grey fuzz of a scratch-card nail. The things we said inside the whale. Prostrate before the turning sail. The something and the something else. Betrayal of, betrayal from. Look over, through or set upon. The double dream, the double glaze, a less bad way out of the maze. Sometimes the action cannot match a long recalibrating daze. And sometimes, sometimes even when I'm the only one with you I want to text, 'Are you okay? Is this guy bothering you?'

Is flattery so bad if it's offered for no reason? I'll drink whatever you give me. If you mean to poison me I believe you ultimately have your reasons. It has nothing to do with trust. You're the absolute best. You're so wonderful. I love you. Everything about you. Really, what do we want from one another? Have you ever been there? Yes. No. How amazing. I bet it was. I bet you were. I heard it was something of an armpit. Yes, but *what* an armpit. In 3rd century Bavaria the armpit was considered – against a backdrop of numerous natural disasters and the breakdown of the internal trade network – the most beautiful part of the human body. Really? Because I thought that was the knee; I thought Bavaria was established in the 18th century. That's nonsense. It became a stem duchy in 602. It's always existed. It was settled by Iron Age Celts before Christ. You know so much about Bavaria. Here, drink this. At that time they practiced *via negativa*: fifty teachers in a room with one student; all holiday and twenty days of work; everyone was a king or queen and went around in finery and crowns, except this one guy: their loyal subject. Everybody's loyal subject. And that's you. I don't think that's what *via negativa means*. But keep going and we'll get there. It is unseemly to dig with your hands while wearing a crown. Even a paper one. Drink up.

I was taking some time off from being a decent and reasonable person. Is not a defence. There was a story about a prince who, when granted a wish, wished to feel hunger. The prince had only ever known a surfeit and, for want of want, had never known true satisfaction. There is a single grape in the punchbowl. Could be a bath pearl. What I like is to inhabit certain areas, a doorway, say, a fleeting sense of camaraderie, what I like is to be *in the way* with such conviction, against the wet paint and the wet paint sign. What it's like is interest on a temporary overdraft. We are young precisely once. A look across a crowded room. A playlist curated with all the everloving hunger. There was a story about a rich man with a burgeoning stock portfolio who, when granted a wish, wished for debt. You want a solid foundation, but you get placed under a baby mobile to keep you occupied. You want to disappear into the night with all the apology of a firework.

Oh really? More? Another one? A day-old sun comes up on the party. It is the era of dark carpets. Somewhere it is always an era in the age of eras and you don't get to choose it, it just engulfs you. The wallpaper is a shaded shop-soiled moon, Demois or Phobos which translates as *Stupid* and *Lumpy*. Era of smoking indoors under bone-yellow ceilings. Of highlighting every line of every page. Era of repairing smashed ornaments with a fag in your mouth. My love for you is like an opened can of Heineken, sipped twice then used as an ashtray several hours ago. That's terrible but I'm hungover – too much to pour the cans down the kitchen sink; I put them in a bin liner which trails a leak across the carpet too dark to show the stain. What I want is to roll over and find you and to want each other but it is the era of ghost hunts and taking measurements and somewhere, through night-vision goggles, your guardian angel is watching someone making a minor adjustment which will one day lead them to you.

They have framed photographs of bookshelves where the bookshelves used to be. They have framed photographs of ex-lovers where, *and so on.* I lead you from one room to another. One season collapses exhausted into the lap of another. You lead me like we're crossing a busy road. I was so upset about something I knew to be petty, and self-awareness is brake-fluid and you were so sweet to me I laughed. What would we do without the backspace key? We'd keep going. There is no backspace key. Someone has got all of the recipe books down and we're just reading recipes to each other and saying, oh that sounds *so* good. Too grateful, even if the secret to happiness is to love one another's irritation, tiredness, silences and evasions because it makes us feel better about our own.

Because influence is indelible you should choose your company carefully. At a party that's impossible. The trouble is I could say something I don't even remotely mean like *Ugh I hate it when people say Hey instead of Hi it's such an affectation or Liking this band is a real red flag – only manipulative people like this band* and if you read it you might think what a crank, who put sour milk in *his* coffee, but some other part, a part that barely distinguishes or fails to filter, would take it in, and you'd take it on as if it was useful or important advice in our generalised dance around judgement, no matter who I am to you. And then, whenever you said Hey instead of Hi or heard somebody, anybody, saying Hey instead of Hi you'd feel a tiny bead of shame, like the first raindrop on your nose, you'd think, Ugh, some people think that's *such* an affectation, we shouldn't do it. It stains like pollen, is what I'm saying. Hey.

II

I had a dream that there were ten of you and we lived in a duplex overlooking the river. It was the only nice part of town. I wanted to make ten of you happy, but it was difficult and mostly I felt like I was letting at least eight of you down. Even though the ten of you were exactly you and exactly the same, you cannot stroke ten people's hair and tell them they are good, they are so good, and oh the divergent seconds where lived experience changed you. Even the inanities, *I love what you've done to your hair. Is that a new top? Could you just shift over a little?* I didn't think I was up to the job. So this is a *job* for you? I don't want to make any special claims here: nobody ever walked down to a river without at least considering taking a dive. We only owned nine mugs, for instance, and it only struck me years later, snow-fishing in a void I'd learned to wrap around myself, how easy it would have been for me to do something about that.

Language, although it's not said so often, is actually brilliant. I mean just look at it. We took too many pointers from depressed short story writers when really language is so wonderful I can only celebrate it sub-lingually, I'll rub my wings together or something. I'm just going to come right out and say: that's not a good reason to have a son. It never even occurred to me. I only want to be temporary custodian of a soul as strange as mine. But I know you're trying to say something nice. Honestly I like you and you're beautiful. If you climb this hill it will make you very old. Meet my replacement in the world; I think he's upstairs playing on my phone. I cannot accept the role of head of department because my contract stipulates I avoid any role which could be described as "Oedipally significant". In one room a man stands by the dimmer switch, slowly turning it all the way up then all the way down repeatedly. Not so much a fantasy as a mistake, and a barely plausible one at that. Tell him to quit it.

One thing guaranteed to kill a party is when people take out their phones and start sharing amusing films with each other. This was never an issue in the 90s, but in the 90s it killed a party when someone brought out a guitar. So I don't expect you to forgive me when I find a guitar in the second bedroom and use my phone – on which plays a film of me playing the same song, yesterday – as a plectrum. Unless everyone's going to sing. Then it's fine. Otherwise, I don't know. Performance and humiliation. Years ago, at a party, a man I was in love with used to read the (bad) short stories I gave him, even though I gave them to him at a party, which was hardly the time or place. Once he asked me to read a paragraph out loud and stopped me because, he said, I was insulting my own writing; and he was right, I was, and with good reason. We disagreed over the existence of God and he would get so angry if I apologised after an argument he'd just walk away.

All I'm saying is that it's selfish of you not to have children because you are so wonderful you're essentially depriving future generations of the chance to meet you. And I know what you're thinking: *What if I died? The person I married would be so fucking sad without me.* But that's a bullshit excuse and you know it. There should be more of you, the world should never be without you, I mean that more than anything I've ever said, dear god has someone spiked this? What if we secretly wound each other's watches back and missed our trains because suddenly the thought of you leaving is unbearable? What if we swapped places and went back to one another's lives with such conviction nobody noticed?

Back in the kitchen the same man is claiming he can recite the plot synopsis of any episode of *Star Trek: the Next Generation* from memory if someone gives him the season and episode number. 'Okay,' I say, 'S4E16.' He glares at me. 'In *Star Trek: The Next Generation*, S4E16, an episode entitled Galaxy's Child, the engineer who developed the Enterprise's engines visits the starship as an honoured guest. Geordi La Forge is nervous because he is in love with a Holodeck version of her which he built and goes to visit all the time which, in itself, is kind of creepy. The way he acts around the *real* her is even worse... I mean... they have profound shared interests and they're both attractive. But, as his flirtation becomes more obtrusive, it emerges that she's married and Geordi gets super pissy about it. He grudgingly collaborates with her to save the ship from some kind of giant space whale. In the final scene *she* apologises to *him*, as if she's the one responsible for his unprofessional conduct. It's mad, but in a way I think I just *absorbed without question* when I first saw it as a ten-year-old boy. He fancies her therefore has ownership. The fact that it's aged so badly and that you watch it now thinking mostly about the men in the writer's room, makes it, if nothing else, a useful document.' We applaud. 'S5E25,' I say.

There is a study, and strictly speaking the study is off-limits; just being in here feels like a small duplicity, ducking under a red rope. We are dismantling the laser printer. You tell me how the cylinder in a laser printer is really an echo of the cylinder-seals used in Mesopotamia in 3,500BC to print symbols onto clay and thereby certify documents. You beat the cylinder against your palm like an impatient juggler waiting for their turn to busk – it leaves soot-lines. I much prefer BC, I say, you *would*, you say. The history of civilisation can be summed up in the following statement: *New and lower-cost methods of reproduction have been developed* by which we mean *class struggle*. Sometimes you meet someone you thought had long gone out of print, but probably we ought to redefine our expectations of a respectable run.

There is a lot to be said for accepting that time is linear, the ageing process, your own mortality. May you live to have grey hair, etc. You have gone upstairs with a flower-arranger. She was wearing a T-shirt emblazoned with the slogan *Moments are the elements of profit* in metallic grey. I am the kind of person who says metallic grey instead of silver. I am sitting on the windowsill and talking to a physicist who is never usually so sociable and therefore I feel sort of honoured – go me! I'm really making him feel comfortable somehow! He says, 'I could catch when I was four years old, but I only learned about vector calculus in my mid-20s. So *now* when I catch it's a more meaningful experience.'

Husband is just a weird metaphor anyway, isn't it? As if wife had its root in *field*. The whole damn thing is a set-up. A terrible man is here – who brought him? We are not used to negotiating him. Please take him away. Before I say what may only be the third stupidest thing I've said tonight I find a cold beer frozen to the back of the fridge and chip it away with a surprisingly rigid packet of cheese slices. Lord, in its sheer relentlessness, hear our prayer. If we were reasonable, but we are not. The only thing I disagree with is the idea that anything at all might make any one of us happy, but it's easy to take that the wrong way and paint me as some kind of monster. I just don't believe in self-actualisation until I meet someone I really like and it strikes me that they're actually themselves. If you're working night shifts you have no right to get annoyed by the noises your correctly-oriented neighbours make in the mornings, but that doesn't mean you won't.

It was always difficult to get anywhere near you because your eyes displayed the future. Word about this got around quickly. People would look into your eyes and think about something which was troubling them and, reflected back, a bright mirror in a dull shop window, they'd see a scene unfold in which some resolution, succour or respite occurred for them and they would leave you happy. In your corneas: *a blue car drives down a long empty dirt track; a woman arrives at a station, out of breath; people emerge from an Arrivals gate one by one, scanning the crowd. One face lights up like a pinball table, they let go of their wheelie suitcase which rolls away and they run towards you, eager to look into your eyes and see their future.* All of this is a place-holder for a true apology. All of this is to say I made someone my religion and it was terrible for me, for them and for religion generally.

Sometimes I say, quietly, out loud, the beginnings of imperatives or peremptories, *I'm going to*— *We need to*— without any sense of how they ought to end. Therefore they express absolutely nothing or they express a nothingness where an intention ought to be. There is a broken blue chair in the garden. Life should be like the moment in a play where they bring on the broken blue chair and everyone applauds. It's little wonder we used to have the very strange ideas we still have. It's little wonder the plants put in so much effort. Fuck yeah, broken blue chair, bring on the broken blue chair. If you had a son he'd be as confused as you.

We're mixing gin with lemon Fanta and talking about the
problem with posterity, about which we all have our own
ideas whilst harbouring secret desires for a *Collected* in ten,
twenty, thirty years' time. Nobody wants to admit to being
part of the problem because believing that you are part of
the problem is profoundly uncomfortable. Also some things
are just embarrassing; some things are just between you and
yourself, but to write is to tell someone to go long and hurl
that part of yourself towards them. Frequently I'd curse God
and die but then privately I'd say, 'I am so, so sorry, God,
I'm so sorry.' Nobody ever puts away childish things because
1. There are so many of them, and 2. There isn't adequate
storage space. The way, in front of friends, I might have
said, 'Yeah, that toy cat is so stupid!' and tossed it down the
stairs. Then later, alone, I'd cradle the toy cat in my arms
and whisper, 'Please forgive me. Please. I'm so sorry.'

Chesterfield's Act of 1750 introduced the Gregorian calendar, already used by the majority of Europe, to Great Britain, losing us eleven days. In order for us to get into sync, 1751 was only 282 days long. Up to that point, the year began on March 25th, the Feast of the Annunciation. Lady Day. This is why, to this day, the tax year begins on April 6th, which, on the Old Style calendar, is March 25th. That's wild, right? So the darling buds of May are actually shaken by the rough winds, in the 16th century, on July 17th, The Day Lady Died, 1959. I don't know if this is as important as it feels, but it feels important insofar as we might compare one another to a necessary adjustment which has unintended repercussions far beyond the administrative.

One useful mental exercise is to lie sleepless and say, Do your worst. So I lose everyone and everything. So I become profoundly resentful and embittered. So I lose the ability even to laugh at myself. So what? So I'm in pain here, here and here. So what? So the side-effects are, at times, worse than the symptoms. So I don't know how much longer I can stand it. So what? So we'll spatchcook the phoenix. So there will be no last-second reprieve. So I will not bear it gracefully – I'll whine. I'd rather save your soul than mine. So I won't inspire anyone, a coward to the last. So what? That my ability to express even this will desert me. That my kindness and forbearance I'm so proud of will last as long as a paper wall in an action movie set improbably during a tea ceremony. But spare her.

That man, you tell me, as we return to the snack table, has used up his soul. There are lots of things we see as infinite resources, but they're *not*. That's harsh, I say. What about me? Oh, you'll always be fine, you fucking arsehole. You kiss me on the nose. You're just being kind, I say. You open a bag of Pop Chips. Oh hell yeah, I say, Pop Chips. I take two handfuls. Nothing is fair, exactly. I remember once I was talking to a colleague and felt, quite without warning, overcome with affection, as if I could see some kind of great purity and goodness in him which nothing could corrupt, not ever. I just smiled at him like a fool and I'm not sure if he noticed. It's something I haven't felt before or since and I don't know if it was, in any way, personal. It's all very well to say go off with anyone but love *me*. It is.

How you behave at a party is actually the most important thing, because a good party is always lit like a therapist's practice or a backstage area. Sometimes you're going to think, what am I going to say, what on earth am I going to say? It was never my intention… Well what was? Make a list. We're only here because of a million accidents. We do things like skip town and join the merchant navy. I remember talking to my dad about his grandfather, who died before he was born. It was a shame, we agreed, that he never met him, but then if he hadn't died when my grandmother was 16 she wouldn't have been left to her own devices, wouldn't have gone out dancing, wouldn't have met my father's father, and neither of us would exist to be having this conversation. Because love is a baby and you are also a baby, you know?

Probably the worst company are the people who lament *the lost art of conversation*. Let's say you take upon yourself a platitude: You are drawn to unattainable people. The sort of phrase so overgrown with moss and lichen it can barely pass for insight anymore. We cannot love ourselves any more than a camera can love itself. We only want something distant enough to be idealised. Thank you. No, don't light it, I want to pontificate with it. We navigate by the North Star because its position happens to be more or less in line with the Earth's axis. In fact it is exactly one degree off and traces a very small arc in the night sky. Nonetheless, it holds fast over bad waters for the tea merchant and the human trafficker. *Let the war criminal say I never claimed to be perfect.* Let's say, *ffs, nobody ever asked for perfection.* What's required of us is the absolute bare minimum, I know. You know the Elizabethan marriage ceremony was quite severe? 'I require and charge you, as you will answer at the dreadful day of judgment when the secrets of all hearts shall be disclosed...' I mean mix that with your confetti, right? We edited it because we're so pathetic. But memory is the present's diet, exclusively, since our hopes' ingredients are memories anyway. That's neuroscience. No, wait, come back.

I wrote so many references today I can't stop describing everyone I meet as reliable and punctual and intelligent and a great communicator. I am sure they will continue to conduct themselves thus as they enter the professional sphere. As they are absorbed by a bright green gelatinous floating sphere, I have every confidence that they will retain atoms of their personality up to and including the ability to love and to be loved. We praise to sell, okay, but also because that's what the empty box requires of us. It's all plumbing, it's all making sure it flows. You could do a book without blurbs but it would look sort of undressed. You could do a book without acknowledgements because thanking people presupposes anyone else is going to like it. So it was when we were young we wouldn't stop talking until someone clamped their hand over our mouths and then we'd lick their hand. All the little birthday candles in heaven. Crooner voice: *God wanted me to know / I am the lowest of the low.* Maybe we all carry a low-key torch for the hard-drinking writing tutor without a good word to say about anyone. *Because when he compliments you he really means it, you know?* But really. Better to put his head on a stick.

The hearts, roughly the size of footballs on chicken legs, running blindly through a forest. The hearts, hunted for sport. The hearts, factory-farmed for food. The hearts, kept as idiosyncratic pets by rich idiots. The hearts sitting at miniature school desks in front of a whiteboard with a diagram of a brain on it. The hearts, breast-feeding in a dimly lit room just to keep them quiet not because they're hungry. The hearts, asking for the same song over and over again. The hearts, finally exclaiming *What more do you fucking want from me?* The hearts, drinking wine from hourglasses. The hearts standing outside their wood-frame houses while a heart with a clipboard unloads a truckload of hearts and says, *Here are the hearts you ordered.* The hearts trying to explain their process because you *did* ask even though they can tell they're boring you. The hearts letting their hair down for once. The hearts, at a sleepover playing Never Have I Ever. The hearts, I'm done, I'm done, I'm done, sorry.

I'm trying to articulate exactly what makes me a bad actor aside from lack of training and experience. I can read a story to my kids with absolute conviction and do the voices. I can read a poem out loud because I know what to play down. When you read a poem all that's required is that you be yourself but worse. But if I have lines and a character and other people depending on my performance it's just awful and everyone feels embarrassed for me. An English busker may put on an American accent if the song is American; this is something we can only forgive ourselves. A good actor reading a good poem sounds terrible because they hit every note too well. Good actors can only read bad poems. Aside from all that, I am fascinated by line-reading and the way a great cast could make bad dialogue lastingly poignant and affecting. If someone says *I love you* there is a moment – *there* – where you get to choose exactly how to deliver your response.

There is a large framed print of Caravaggio's *Judith Beheading Holofernes* (c. 1598-1599) on the landing. 'Consider the very limited range of expressions in visual art,' you say to me. The eyes in a portrait say *I am being painted* the way the eyes in a photograph say *I am being photographed* and any exception is first and foremost a happy accident but simultaneously the only proof of the human soul. So the trick is somehow not to know, but this is less about self-ironizing ('I love you.' 'That's stupid.') as it is to allow some indication that you are known and understood by the painter or the photographer. Something furtive, ill at ease, between the studio and frame-maker and the gallery. There is much that cannot be reconciled with the historical record. The Gentileschi is too good, and the second, attributed Caravaggio is a biscuit tin. But this is the right one: the blood is red ribbons in a school play, Holofernes a rubber fright-mask, the attendant a coin profile on the currency of a dour country. But I have never been able to stop thinking about the model who plays Judith. She wields the scimitar firmly and holds his hair like a rope in a pulley, having sliced halfway through his neck already. Her expression, though, is more intimate than an aside to-camera. Somewhere between irritation and amusement

– like she's solving a complex equation or taking a precise measurement or trying to remember, for a moment, what she ever saw in you.

A vassal sends a letter but it gets intercepted and altered and his title is abolished during long-overdue land reforms. Yes yes yes yes. Sometimes when you get to a new city it feels small and you wonder what you were so worried about. I don't have anything to add. The vassal sends another letter but it's hopeless and he cannot adapt or find his place in the new regime so he becomes a holy fool, but even then he sends a letter asking permission to become a holy fool which is, his contemporaries grudgingly concede, at least a foolish thing to do. Maybe it's odd to think about duty and obligation at a party, but maybe you feel like a Sim. My half-time team-talk references the death of King David's illegitimate son after a prolonged illness. Which makes it, in the words of my tactical manager, a *bad* half-time team-talk. King David took off his sackcloth and sat down to a feast and got drunk and when his courtiers asked him what had become of his piety and resolve and fasting he just shrugged and said, 'The boy is dead.'

The crying man is drunk and supported by the mantelpiece. He's saying: Ultimately you want to convince someone of their own worth beyond any doubt, to the point that there's not a chance in hell they'd stay with you when they've seen the real you. The crying man is chubby and muscular and not unattractive: *slabby*. We say: Woah there, pal, why don't you come and sit down. You are valued, you are loved. But it gets lost in the lyrics to 'Miss American Pie' and he waves us off. And he's right – we don't even know him. For all we know he could be a terrible person and everyone would be better off without him. We give him the little plastic Freud action figure from the mantelpiece, we tell him: But for the disturbance of self-regard, mourning and melancholia are very similar. You are exhausted by the inner work, you are not eating or sleeping, but also, you must surely be *right* in some way. You have "a keener eye for truth than other people who are not melancholic." Our sole aim is to hide our weaknesses. The difference, when you dig deep enough, is that in melancholia you do not really know what you have lost, you're just digging, you just keep on digging, you just—

We went on a pilgrimage and when we reached the destination we saw many miracles. An uncreated light descended upon us; a loaf of bread got no smaller however much we ate of it; hundreds touched a worn out indentation of a foot in a rock and went off healed.

Or we went on a pilgrimage and when we reached the destination we saw wooden boxes containing fragments of bone. An attendant shooed us away. The smell of lavender could not camouflage the open sewers. Outside, we stopped to stroke a stray cat but it scratched us and the scratches puffed up like zippers. We developed a fear of water which is a sure sign of rabies. The meal was mostly fat our knives could not cut through. That was when, sharing a single bed narrower than a single bed, the pilgrimage continued, or when it started, I don't know. We closed our eyes. If you orbit a black hole and watch someone else floating into it, they will appear to you to stop, completely still, at the threshold forever. In just this way we move, ever slower, towards ourselves.

Drunkenness and sobriety, mania and depression, night and day; a truce between all opposites if they can make us suffer more. Let them be the protagonists to our treachery. Let one turn up at the eleventh hour to the other's aid when they were all but vanquished by our cruel and starving army. When we finally had one on the gallows may the other ride in on horseback, cut them down and leave a pike stuck in our stomach as the credits roll. May the heroic juror stick it out to the last and somehow derail our show trial. Blargh. Inside me there are two wolves and I don't feed *either* of them. It's a long night, and we can make it longer. I've got a blank space…

I have lost one of my shoes. All that follows is spoken by a man wearing one shoe. 'You seemed very comfortable with the brain surgeon.' 'She's a neuroscientist.' 'Whatever.' 'We're just friends. I was lonely. Her clothes were very smooth.' You make a cocktail and call it Amygdala Hijack. Oh poor me. Poor you. Observers of our own predicament. Lads on tour chanting *God will forgive us!* How far you can fall in everybody's estimation is proportional to the silent claims you always made on them. Nonetheless, I think of you and wouldn't change place with anyone. Lying is one of the most sophisticated operations of the prefrontal cortex. The Liar Paradox is only unresolvable in languages which are semantically closed. We needn't moralise. In the end to lie is to choose a meaningless universe. No-one's saying it's easy to be honourable, but if you're *not* you find yourself in uncharted territory and it's scary. It's scary, man. I am saying this on stage at a book festival to the six people in the audience. They are looking at me like a sell-by date. *Does cream of tartar even go off?* You can't change anything once it's published. Afterwards I sign one book. The man tells me to make it out to myself and to rewrite it to include this scene. On the three hour drive home the clutch feels deep and chewy under my bare foot. An M40 diversion ejects me like a bad idea and I end up going round in circles in the Vale of Evesham until I run out of petrol outside a walled garden. I can see lanterns, I can hear a string quartet, and the gate is open.

After some time we got tired of going to the same parties but kept going. *I'm so sorry to miss you. I'm so sorry I can't make it.* But then we'd turn up anyway. We'd make an excuse then we'd turn up and not explain it. People got used to that. Or we'd insert ourselves into memories whenever they were recounted until people couldn't say for sure if we'd been there or not. *We all got into the bath and took off our clothes and turned the shower on and passed around a bottle of Cava as if we'd just won a match or something.* Yes – we were there too – we opened the bottle. It was a pleasure to watch them frown and try to place us, then acquiesce at our insistence. That's how we lived as ghosts, sucking on petrol soaked rags for appetite suppressants. How do you think you'll look back on this once every debt's repaid? You'll pay them again. Hey baby I hear the blues are calling...

Some cannot help the way they're feeling, some can. Some are hawks, some are horses. Horses believe we are all essentially the same; hawks know better. Horses fear the broken cobble stones; hawks try to avoid large bodies of water. Horses have the largest eyes of any land mammal, they see all apples as green and their retina is called the Nervous Tunic; hawks can perceive the ultraviolet part of the spectrum and magnetic fields. They can use their indented fovea to zoom in on distant objects. Horses: Tuesday; Hawks: Thursday. Their retinue is called a kettle. Horses think they're getting away with it; hawks are aware of every unspoken thing that passes between us. Horses: nosebags; Hawks: hoods. Horses: blinkers; Hawks: fuck in the air as they free-fall down to earth. The strangest thing a human being ever said to a horse is the most sensible thing a human being ever said to a hawk. If you pass by a strange horse and do not say *Oh, a horse*, the horse will take umbrage; hawks have never seen anything more ridiculously beautiful than a bridge.

III

Did they confuse our orders? We met because they confused our orders. It was a restaurant. Or we were in the army. Either way it was inevitable that we would meet exchanging plates or inscrutable codes over the border. We met because we joined the same cult and escaped together just before the shooting started. It was a cult we co-founded, but so conveniently wrong for us. We met at a party, this party, some other party. We met when the cult begged us to re-join because it wasn't the same without us.

Sometimes nostalgia is just a self-microwaving cup of coffee which will never cool sufficiently to bring it to your lips. A build-up to the first kiss like a ski-lift; on a ski-lift. As a child I felt it necessary to apologise for being a child. As an adult not so much. Sometimes it is necessary to retrace your steps just in case you find yourself lying by the side of the river. It's fun until it isn't. Sometimes nostalgia can be likened to a man who owns a vineyard. He goes down to the marketplace to find workers to gather the grapes, but instead... how does it go? They kill him and his son and set fire to the vineyard. There was a moral. We met because there was a moral.

How we behave in a church, if that's our thing, is interesting.
Better, for a start, to be hungover than drunk, to be in tears
than laughing, to have no idea, really, of your purpose.
Conduct yourself accordingly. Better to turn up straight
from the party and brush yourself down by the narthex. We
oughtn't see *conducting ourselves* as disingenuous, because
we are all terrible orchestras. There are two kinds of irony
to choose between: one is that you are struggling with your
tuba on the underground during rush hour; one is that
you are a freemason, how do you do. I fear God, I nod
liturgically towards God. There are so many gradations one
hardly notices. You don't know anyone. No, wait, you do.

Sometimes, in a gift shop, we might choose a shark's tooth in a little clear plastic box. A particular tooth might catch our eye, among the pieces of fool's gold, rose quartz, amethyst. A single shark loses *thousands* of teeth a year. What were we curating on our bedside shelves? I loved fool's gold. I'd take it out and look at the tiny perfect cube formations and just think *how?*

How was your date? It was terrible. All he talked about was bones. Did you know that babies have more bones than adults? Because some of them haven't joined together yet? I guess. I sort of tuned out. He didn't ask me *one* thing about myself apart from if I'd ever broken a bone. Have you? No. Motherfucker seemed *disappointed.* Babies have 300 bones, apparently. Look, I'm not comfortable sympathising with bad dates – I have no idea if I'm a good date and I tend to just use the opportunity to feel better about myself at some poor sucker's expense. Like when someone's ill – I'm all, Oof, *I'm* not ill, that's nice. It's not a good part of me.

Name me one thing that doesn't cloud over. *Do you think you can hide anything from me?* I think you can look at me long enough and I'll evaporate. Like the song about songs. Like the song of all songs. Like the song of all songs about songs. When I was five another boy tricked me into looking at the sun; I knew he was lying, I did it anyway. If she be a wall... and if she be a door... festooned with cedars. I asked the watchmen that go about the city, solemn and drunk, I founded a police state in your honour. You're looking very dapper. Thank you. The theologian holds forth on the window seat. *A collection of love poems spoken alternately by a man and a woman... Solomon's name is a later addition, nobody knows the true author... there is no coherent story...* I have compared thee, o my love, to a company of horses. Strengthen me with raisins renew me with apples. Crescent moon of the sun-stained apple. The light on your brow. Air brackets. You are rabbits digging holes in mountains of spices. Your hair is mountain goats running down the crevasse. All night I searched the bed for you. When we were singing to each other it was good, it was good while it lasted, a fountain sealed, a spring shut up. How much better is thy love than wine. The ugly rack of clouds winched off the set for the next matinee. Or not at all, vulgar collusion of the metaphor. How every analogy passes over you like a cloud, as temporary, thank God, as trivial. Cause me to hear it.

It was so nice earlier we didn't wear coats and anyway wanted some pretext to link arms. And who are you really angry with when you're angry with the weather? Once in a museum my son spilled juice all over his top and I hadn't brought a change of top for him. He was shivering and uncomfortable. I was wearing a T-shirt and a jacket, so I took off his wet top and put my T-shirt on him, which reached the ground, and then had to wear my jacket – a blazer, really, but I hate the word blazer – done up and clutched to my throat so I didn't look like some member of a failed boyband twenty years later. This is unremarkable and anyone would have done the same, I guess – I mean you're not going to say, You spilled the juice, you have to put up with it, that's just cruelty, and anyway you were the one who forgot to prepare for every eventuality.

Sometimes the long drive is better than the party. Don't feel bad. Your best shoes pinch. A good nap makes you tireder still. Completing a level of a game you're playing for fun just gives you another, harder level. A gorgeous poem often has some mawkish lines. Kind people forget to look after themselves and snap. When we try to be funny it is, sometimes, not funny. The best oranges are hard to peel. Ringing endorsements often miss the point. Some beautiful views have factories. Some beautiful factories have views. If you put a good dog in a room with a bad dog you just get a bad room of dogs. Even Occam's razor sometimes nicks the skin. The best analogies are compromised. Even in writing this I'm implicated; it's like I'm trying to excuse something reprehensible but you give yourself such a hard time and the least I can do is fall down the same well.

What was I *thinking*, standing on the balcony. It was where I started writing. To dream a balcony means you need support or peace. I was standing on the balcony. It was there I realised I was right next to my hotel, the one I thought I'd have to take a taxi to. Its logo reflected in my hiball glass. I was thinking *the law of all motion is to always involve one another in interesting situations* when I struck my forehead on the corner of a glass door just hard enough to draw blood, a single line that ran around my eye. Now the homeopath will treat me but only if I fall in love with her. 'I'm not a homeopath – I study the history of homeopathy.' Sorry. Reciprocal affection must exist between the doctor and the patient; "Syrups and juleps have very little inherent virtue", as Eliphas Levi says. Now this is also how we see each other: if you love me, keep my commandments; if you love me you will believe in the memory of the substance in the water. I check my drink and the hotel logo is still there. She gives me two tiny white pills. Let's talk about how you can't enjoy anything. What did the angel in hell say to the demon in heaven? Whispered into a contact microphone. Changing the subject so often indicates an unquiet mind. Fourth opinion. I don't know, what did the demon in heaven say to the angel in hell? No single object can fully

and permanently contain the images to which it is related.
You are watering the plants, your ears stopped with wax.
Cara mia ti amo, solo tu, solo tu, solo tu, solo tu.

Far worse, of course, if there were ten of *me*. Five would be moody, tearing the labels off our beer bottles, four would be bursting with ideas – *Shall we look for a new flat? Can you help me hand-bind these pamphlets?* – and naturally I'd see myself as the most important me despite the other nine all claiming to be the original, to the point where you wouldn't know anymore. We'd all drawn Xs on our foreheads. If I ever got any time with you alone I'd weep and say *You have to believe me. We have to find some way of getting rid of them.* You'd have heard that from each of us in turn. *One of me keeps eating my ramen noodles and I'm not sure if it's one of the sad ones or one of the happy ones.* There is only so much up-tempo college rock you can listen to in one sitting. We'd all get colds at the same time. We'd say, *I feel like a father*, as if it was the worst thing. Once you'd left us we'd really turn on one another. *Is it remotely surprising?* We'd eat cold pizza with cigarettes stubbed out in the middle. We'd barely look each other in the eye.

In the living room we play a game where we work out how many years, strictly speaking, we ought to be in jail for, Googling maximum sentences for the petty crimes for which we were never caught or to which we never confessed, assuming the imaginary judge is having a bad day. I never shoplifted in the pure sense, but once – no, *twice*; the second time it didn't work – swapped the label on a CD I wanted so I could pay a lower price. Fare-skipping. Trespassing. A little light perjury. Some are in deeper: Kevin, for instance, should never see the light of day again. After going through multiple counts of possession for class A, B and C drugs we're all pretty much dead of old age in our cells even though none of us would identify as drug users, per se. Generally we see anything we do wrong as quite out of character, exceptions which prove our overall decency and for which no punishment is necessary, which is privilege in action, which is why we feel grateful and ashamed a lot of the time and also why we are ridiculous.

–What's problematic is the novelty of someone finding you worth seducing. –Problematic for whom? –If you spent your formative years considering yourself essentially undesirable and all interpersonal experience seemed to confirm that. –(Boo hoo). –I know. It's intoxicating when someone thinks you're attractive. –Thinks? –Finds, then. – It doesn't really excuse anything. –No. It explains it. –I don't know if it even explains it. –I think it's a way to look at it. –I think all anyone wants to know is that they could have you if they wanted. Consummation is optional. –Really? That's sad. I don't think anyone's that calculating. –Power more than desire. They are. We are. –Well maybe lust for power's the only vice I don't have in abundance. I'm naturally submissive. –That's just another kind of power. –Uh huh? –A big, soft, lazy one. And a dodge. –As if to say, it is not fair to try to seduce me because I am so weak. –Right. It's a pretty old line. –Do you remember apple-bobbing? I think I only did it once in the youth centre when they got a big enough vat from somewhere. I can't remember if you'd just go right in there and bite straight away or if you had to sort of pin an apple to the side of the vat with your chin and… –Do you think they have apples here?

You put your head in your hands and tell me you have a life-ruining crush on every single person at the party. Ah, I say, How sweet it is to be in love, and how interesting to know that you are in love. "That, after all, is something no art, no study, can reproduce." But isn't love born of scarcity? Mustn't there be some element of finding someone you can set the world against? How can it pertain to a crowded room? It should make everyone else fade away, porch sophists with their vapid bromides: *Are you following me?* They teach virtue to young salesmen. You tell me everyone here is worth seducing. Look at him. You point at the economist. No, I say, You only love the economist because I do. Before I expressed interest in the economist you had never given him or his nice arms a second glance. There is, in fact, an economic theory he told me about which expresses exactly this situation; it's called— I love the economist, you tell me, who, by the way, I would never reduce to his vocation, because he is doomed, because he believes he can extract a wave from the ocean and still call it a wave. I love him, and his noble failures, in ways you couldn't begin to understand.

From the opposite side of the room you wink at me. Signal. In the West, the wink is supposed to indicate some shared hidden knowledge, solidarity or flirtation, dependent on context. Nobody agrees on its origins. In Africa the wink can be a code parents use to ask children to leave the room when adults are visiting and want to have a conversation. Children are supposed to know this and to absent themselves unprompted, so the wink functions to save face for all parties concerned. But once the wink just meant to sleep or to look the other way, to deliberately overlook flaws. Idealisation is either a gift we give each other or a dangerous mirage. Look at the open eye: the pool, the portal. A thirty year life-within-a-life during which no time elapses. In a Hindu legend a pool is discovered that converts female into male, male into female. When I was a child I had a cat from the Cats' Protection League. She was called Pasca. She hated being stroked, but liked it if you sat on the other side of the room and slowly closed and opened your eyes – a gesture she'd mimic and, after a while, start purring.

I have a friend who breaks into uncontrollable screaming at the first sign of small talk. *How are you doing?* is enough. I find him shaking by a fire extinguisher. I try to get him onto a subject he can talk about. "What can we say of this fanciful classification of humours into four groups, of which two are absolutely imaginary?" – Charles Richet, 1910. My friend is a medical historian, and what comforts him is the sound of a hair dryer. I take him by the hand and we try to find one in the host's bedroom. I plug it in. The trouble with drinking whiskey is you need to go back to the bar so frequently. Legerdemain. The bedside table jolts of its own accord. Richet was into extra-sensory perception. He was a eugenicist. I suppose, as a medical historian, you encounter that quite a lot. He looks at me and turns the hairdryer off. It's killing me, he says. Extracting jellyfish toxins. He mutters, A violent reaction killed the dog. *Vas inane*: my loyalty is to whomsoever I happen to be speaking at the time. I turn the dryer back on and stroke his hair. Recently I accidentally used an old binbag, the glue corroded at its seal, so that when I pulled it out of the bin it just drew straight out like a sleeve, leaving a giant bin two-thirds full of festering garbage. I was so affronted by this I can only conclude it was somehow symbolic.

Let's leave him there. A couple are lounging on the staircase.
This man is wearing a nice watch. I tell him that it's a nice
watch. Are watches just an inheritance tax dodge? I'm torn
between finding expensive watches a vulgar and offensive
status symbol and respecting the craft of the watchmaker,
which is undeniably something beautiful, isn't it? Shouldn't
people be able to become watchmakers if they want to? I
mean should we tell them *not* to? Their eye-muscles taut
around a loupe in museum-light, their vanquished shoes,
health sacrificed to tweezers too small for human hands
– such *passion*. You can only admire someone who hurts
themselves that much. I've stood in a 2nd hand bookshop
and inhaled the smell of a 1st edition and felt the desire
to own it. If there's a difference it's a small one. I want
the artist's strangest work to sell, I want your poetry to be
adored; does that suppose an audience with leisure time
and self-esteem and means? A patron caste? If so, while I'd
choose public luxury / private deprivation over anything
in the end, and like to think all I aspire to is fairly modest,
what drives the whole damn show? Money? Ugh.

Heart takes eye to the abandoned shopping centre to point out how tall the weeds have grown. Eye leads the heart to the very edge of the platform and says, 'Just to be clear, I'm not like this.' Heart asks eye to come to a narcotics anonymous meeting, but eye's kinda busy. Eye shows heart how to shave an overcoat so you don't get the weird bobbles. Heart says, 'Close your eyes on a long beach and run parallel to the sea as fast as you can until your legs give way.' Eye just spent £38 on a rare Pokémon card at the comic book shop. Heart wants to go somewhere, anywhere. Eye concedes on the condition that Heart gets better at just sitting quietly in a chair sometimes. Heart has well and truly had enough of Eye's bullshit. Eye wants to know why Heart even deserves a voice in the matter anymore, or at least why Heart should expect anyone to listen to them now. Does Heart have any "teachable moments" to monetise? Would Heart, deep down, like nothing more than to be an "Influencer"? If Heart was honest? What does Heart plan to do with their platform now that they have it? Could Heart either keep moving or get out of the way? Could Heart just shut up? Could Heart just absolutely shut up?

IV

She had two horses: an Appaloosa to ride towards nice things or away from bad things; and an American Quarter Horse to ride towards anything she didn't want to do, or to ride away from nice things when it was time to do so. I would dutifully ride whichever horse she wasn't using at the time, sneaking it Polo mints, because the system required that both horses always be present, whatever the affair. I was not a good horse-rider but had accepted my obligations as what you get for marrying "up". My boots were a size too small. I loved the smell of mud in the cool night air. The happy horse was so happy and the sad horse was so sad. One night the sad horse saw an angel blocking our path and was temporarily granted the gift of speech. She was riding ahead on the happy horse and didn't notice. The sad horse told me a story about scientists working to slow down an asteroid on a collision course with Earth. It imagined it was one of the scientists delivering the news after the plan had failed. 'It's still accelerating,' the sad horse had to say to the government, 'but it's not accelerating as fast as it was; forgive us for seeing that as a victory.' 'So it's getting *faster?*' the Chancellor of the Exchequer would say. 'Yes,' the horse would reply. 'It's just not getting faster as quickly as it was before.'

By this point people with a nobler sense of purpose, a more tragic sense of life, have left the party. They have wholesome interests like wild swimming; we have unwholesome interests like co-dependency. A man is blowing his nose on a black napkin. You say, 'Imagine you had to go *off* me.' For what reason? 'For *some* reason. I had to leave you and you had to *get over* me.' So I do. I look at an uneven patch on the wall and I think about it. I imagine it being quite difficult. 'What do you miss about me?' I don't tend to divide people into isolated properties – I miss the whole unified field of you. 'Aw.' But I tend to get quite attached to people anyway. 'You do. Why do you think that is?' As long as someone likes me I can agree with them. If you didn't like me anymore I'd realise you'd seen me for who I really am. 'And who *is* that? Is all of this really about other people's perceptions of you? I don't think you even mean any of this; I think this is a sort of contra-flow defence system.' That sort of thing, yes.

To dedications, per se. That is, you have qualities beyond my ability to describe them. With some people it would be stressful just to take a couple of train journeys, with you I'd happily be lost without a phone in the middle of a strange country – that long bit of France they don't even make maps of, say – and it's the middle of the night and what are we going to do? With some people you can never say what you mean without them misinterpreting it or talking over you before you reach the main clause, with you I'd find going to the supermarket and finding neither of us had a pound for the trolley somehow delightful and also it's raining ball-bearings because metal started evaporating. But isn't our job to honour those who find it hard to say anything or get up, who find the day impassable, as could happen... Whatever. Isn't that to honour a hypothetical love, an overarching fidelity in and of itself, with sciatica, with unpaid bills, with sighing and disappointment in each other. To hold our own discomfort down until its tell-tale death-gurgle the more to calibrate to sense each other's? What we're going to do is spread out my coat under a tree, what we're going to do is knock on the door of the first farmhouse we come to and say *nous avon faime*. Because gradually the more we back away from our own injuries the more precious everyone else becomes to us. Someone should paint you. I'd hate it. I'd say they hadn't captured you at all.

There are two poets at the party, both of them are infatuated with you and both of them are writing poems about you. They're not great, the poems, but they're about you, so they have their moments. One is haunted by the things they said and did when they had a drinking problem. One is tortured by something they said to their sister in 1987. Both kind of forgivable, whether or not you believe in redemption narratives. Occasionally you'd get the two of them together in a loud craft-beer place and you'd say, *Okay, let's get this sorted out once and for all. I'm not so great. I'm honestly not sure what all the fuss is about. My eyes? Seriously?* They'd stare balefully into their opaque beers. *There are plenty of people more intelligent, more considerate, more beautiful than I am,* you'd tell them. *My voice is no better or worse than anyone else's, my sense of humour is serviceable but predominantly reactive, the way I move, the way I* am *in the world is nothing special. What have you isolated, a nose on a silver plate? This is a kind of socially acceptable fetishism. Most of the time I feel nothing, I do very little, I am irritable and focus on my minor ailments. So what is it? Can you name a single specific thing about me that's causing all this heartache?* One of them has started to cry. *Okay,* you'd say, *okay, I'm sorry, god, it's okay, you can be infatuated with me.*

Keep writing about love – I think we're finally about to nail it. I think this is maybe your 12th life. If someone described you accurately it would be seized upon and burned by the state, even a previously benign state. It's too much. Nobody would be satisfied. You'd be surrounded. People would say they just wanted to sit with you for a bit. People would say *You never replied to my email.* Nobody would have any dignity in their pursuit of you. Mild-mannered priests hitting each other with clubs to get to the uncreated light before the other dioceses. Even so. We'd pore over the samizdat. *It's not quite them*, we'd say in our underground book-groups, our worried faces picked out by an oil lamp. *It doesn't quite capture the way they lift their jaw very slightly before responding in a gesture at once ironic and heartfelt, it doesn't make you feel like your heart is in furious motion, it's fundamentally a subjective account of something objective...* We'd hush each other.

'There is a library of everything you've ever said and thought,' the sad horse tells me. 'There's one for everyone. That's what heaven is. It's not very nice.' Each library measures six by four thousand cubits. 'Most people in heaven,' the sad horse scratches the side of its nose against an empty shelf, 'spend eternity trying to find out what other people really thought of them.' There is the sad horse, there is the ghost of the sad horse and there is my idea of the ghost of the sad horse. Only the latter is at the party. We're going to dance. Eleanor Frances Lattimore's *Felicia* (1964) introduces the idea of "temporary transmigration" when a cat becomes a human girl and befriends the protagonist. *Are you happy?* is a loaded question. You find it sometimes, which given that you are in a taxi with a map of the wrong city and you don't speak the same language as the driver, is... How will he know which library to drop you off at? Do not forget to do something mindless when you are subdivided between so many circles. Years ago I read a newspaper article about Victoria Beckham being overheard saying, 'I just need someone to be nice to me today' on a phone and it's stayed with me ever since. Horse light, horse bright, first horse I see tonight. You don't have to say anything.

A party inhearsed, the doors, the hallways closed up like sinuses. A skeleton, I would lie with one hand in yours, the pristine red cups surviving our clothes. Do you remember – I'd say – the house we rented by the forest? A spirit arrived nightly and granted me intelligence, granted me the gift of speech, granted me the ability to understand you.

When you are living in it, the specific red ghosts of your life don't feel like specific red ghosts: it's only when you look back and miss the superior brain-feel. So close you could almost billow the sails again. Where am I? You are in a museum. Trade is named after the trade winds, not the other way around. You get some sense of this when a single evening separates into several epochs. I don't want you to leave. There's no decision. There's nothing to interpret. Sometimes you have to force the words out, smoke in a beehive, sometimes, what must you think of me?

Because life as constant feasting would be monstrous; because what is lost, if the fasting is reduced to a symbolic gesture, is more than self-control, is the capacity to take any joy in the feast, is having set off on a journey at all. I should see you rarely and think of you too often. I leave the room when you arrive. Three moments: 1. I was in London with a journal editor – now folded – and his partner was talking to me about translating Foucault. I hadn't eaten all day and by the evening everything was sparkling and I felt overwhelmed with love as if I could hear my own soul for the first time. 2. Once I over-ate before Vespers and all I could think about – *now that we have come to the setting of the sun and behold the evening light* – was how *full* I was, pinned down to the surface of the planet, a mushroom. 3. For the first three days of Lent one is supposed to eat and drink nothing. My weight fluctuates quickly so by the third day my rings kept shooting off my right hand whenever I made too sweeping a gesture.

Maybe the sad horse is actually the happy horse because it has low expectations of how it will be treated. It says thank you a lot, even when you haven't done anything and I think it means *thank you for not hurting me for no reason. Thank you for not visiting upon me the literal or symbolic violence I am permanently anticipating.* 'School leaves most humans lastingly cowed,' I tell it. 'And if not that, then what passes for love. So I *get* it, sad horse.' The sad horse says thank you. At times like this I want to hold the sad horse's giant head in my arms and say I am so sorry for what you've been through. And we would be happy together. But then... the happy horse has low expectations too. The happy horse has had its portrait painted but the artist has chosen to represent it with six jagged lines and several washes of blue and black. On a tiny canvas. 'Isn't it great?' the happy horse says. 'Don't you love it?' It is standing outside the French windows because it doesn't want to impose. 'And besides, I love the yard.'

Often, facially, the statues of the most beautiful gods... they don't really do it for me. They're blank, they lack intensity, they lack... What? The drunker I get the less respect I have for anybody's discipline. The art historian pinches the bridge of his nose. I take a drink. Take Adonis, I say. Statue Adonis looks like he's choosing an avocado or trying to work out which one's the printer cable. Give me literally anyone laughing or scowling. Give me an hour scrolling Twitter on my phone. Tell me we're not supposed to fancy statues. I have a tendency to get kind of swallowed up by people, or to get swallowed up by how highly I think of them, which is to say, I construct some giant machine capable of swallowing when I could have constructed literally anything else. We spend more time with our ideas of each other than with each other – this is not a problem. Say what you will, the little advent calendar windows into our neuroses are good things. I want to know whatever's on your mind or whatever you're pretending is on your mind or whatever. Are we attracted to people who look sort of offended? I would like a statue to look offended. When I was 18 I went out with a woman who constantly tried to offend me because she found the way I gasped in response arousing. It was wonderful.

It feels like a mixed-metaphor / closed system: That a rose is beautiful is confirmed by the smell of the rose; therefore that you are perfect is confirmed by the fact that it's true: you are perfect. Major histocompatibility complex genes influence who we are drawn to by the way they smell, although I'm not sure. It's maybe that we're not *put off* someone we were drawn to anyway – it could easily go the other way. The way you think about what people say to you and how beautiful you look while you're thinking about it. That's not even a fraction of it, but it's something that takes possession of me. Natural dyes require fixative chemicals called *mordants*. Biting. Dyes and mordants often produced such strong odours that dyeing factories were built even further from their communities than rendering plants. The distinction between *further* and *farther* only pertains to American English. I don't mean to put you on a pedal-stool. It's called a pedestal. It's called a unicycle.

Marble makes a good backdrop for doing pretty much anything, although I tend to dislike street entertainers and I haven't asked myself why. It feels the same as the kid with the knife we let into the party and now he's asked us all to sit on the floor with our hands behind our heads. I think you have some fleeting notion of how remarkable you are – you feel it in a song you love and play to death – but you don't know where the book's taking you; when clothes fit you you don't feel them; you stop seeing the street you live on; you know your voice, you don't know its affect; nobody can perceive how they even smell most of the time. I promise I'll shut up. A statue of you would have its eyes closed and people would only be able to view it blindfolded, but this is better. Eventually we have to let go of everything or give ourselves up to be destroyed, that's a given, it's not worth dwelling on. But nothing can erase who you are right now or who you've been, and you are so much more than you think you are. Nobody is going to leave this room and we are all going to hand over our wallets and phones.

The sea may part us; the sea may part for us. It doesn't matter. Certain things come and go and if it's just the spit of land which emerges periodically and which can cut you off, so be it, haunted empty buses in the mist. But I am never going to feel any differently about you, you know that: a trudge home in the slush, the leaves rotted down and nowhere safe to land, thinking of a summer evening lying on the lawn, someone topping up your glass. You could love anyone, you know? Anyone and their parasol. My favourite memory is of a National Trust gift shop in winter – my father bought me a model of an Egyptian cat. I remember standing in the carpark, the tiny stones frozen into the ground, the texture of trying to scuff them up with the sole of my Hi-Tec trainers, anticipating going home, feeling warm, the cat in its plastic box in my coat pocket, and I have no idea why this is the happiest I have ever been or why it's exactly the way you make me feel, to the last neuron.

New guests arrive as the clubs kick out which is just as well – we were getting sluggish. There are those who want control, who ask you where you've been, there are kites and kite-eating trees. Sometimes you can see how someone mutes the one who loves them like a television. I lean against a wall fantasising about being interviewed, but the interview keeps going wrong and I keep saying stupid and boring things, that's why I'm frowning, that's why when you asked me what I was thinking I was too embarrassed to tell you. Then I fantasise about somebody insulting you and punching them. That is the kind of man I am, I think. Did you see that guy checking you out? Yeah, he was. The naturally submissive are terrible at accepting responsibility and follow the turn of the evening like cats – I'm like that, that's why. Cities where the fountain is the shape it is because the lovers met there and the library is on that corner because that was the corner that was written about in the Book of Corners. You are somewhere else being delighted in, you are somewhere being twice as alive, the warmth of that is stunning. 'I am the bad servant,' says the sad horse, poking his nose between the banisters. 'Nobody comes to ruin except by me.'

Thoughts matter / Thoughts don't – this is the pivotal difference between faith and logical positivism. Seeing as they *do*, let none of my thoughts imprison you. The crying man is still sitting under the mantlepiece. The guests who arrived late from the club smelling of cigarettes and orange juice have gathered around him offering advice. You have to build an igloo. It's sweet, what you're trying to do, but it won't get you anywhere. In fact your thoughts will kill you. Saw your thoughts into blocks and press them together. Let not my thoughts of you imprison you, let not your thoughts of me imprison you. We might extend this – a message is a thought carved into a little block; we have unprecedented access to one another's thoughts and we do not know the repercussions of this yet, we never will.

"All of this has happened before and will happen again." Is that from *Battlestar Galactica*? No. They took it from Peter Pan, who took it from Stoicism. 500 years ago someone who looks a lot like you is talking to someone who looks a lot like me by a low wall. It is a failure of my imagination that I always imagine events in the past taking place in and around ruined buildings. We lived in ruins then. We stirred saucepans under an open sky, hung the ladle on a hook on a piece of devastated wall. We married in ruined churches, worked in ruined typing halls, walked among the blasted columns. We decorated them with ribbons. The only thing missing was the gift shop. As the idea with driving is that eventually you become self-instructing, is it so with therapy that you eventually become self-therapising? How do you feel? Scared. Let's think about where that comes from. Would it not then also be the case that you become increasingly blasé and would fail your test if you had to sit it again?

'Like as the waves make towards the pebbled shore' (60)

Susurration of the shore. Are you still with me? Continue watching. Exit. Remember this conversation forever even if it's only to regret the wasted time. The Chronical of Wasted Time. I am trying so hard to get to something important: how I hate and love everyone in the room, especially me. It was funny, the determination with which we used to visit a pebbled beach and lay our towels out on the shelves of egg-sized, shifting stones. The way we'd walk and sink and twist our ankles down to the freezing sea and stagger around cursing in the shallows, jeans rolled above our knees. Some stones had oil marks which would stain your skin when you fell on them and we supposed they'd tumbled over from a distant oil spill, the kind we saw on the news, the lacquered seagull and the toothbrush. It wasn't really a human beach at all, you couldn't have a gathering there, your flask would roll down to the sea, the tide came in six times a day and drenched your shoes stuffed with your socks and your Timex Indiglo watch – the ones that turned out to be mildly radioactive. The biting insects were adept. It did everything to put us off, the beach, but it had a name and we'd drive there and so would hundreds of others, 45 minutes down a single lane with few passing points so the road would snare with the contraflow, a dozen reversals through gritted teeth. Ok.

V

Before the invention of love it was supposed to emerge from the sacrament of marriage like an activation code, like a scratch card, like a ferret sent down a rabbit hole. The problem with the crying man is that he will say: I miss the ferret, the ferret never came back. Or he will say, Wherever you slept last night, it's nothing to me, and he will mean the same thing. It is good that you have disentangled yourself from him, like a scratch card, like an activation code. He misses you, that's true, but we cannot control our spirits, our ghosts which are every other's version of us held dearly like an activation code, and we cannot help each other at this stage, so he will keep coming back to you, twisting like a ferret. As with many things it is difficult to know what to do or to suggest other than really hope the whole situation sorts itself out somehow.

Like writing, it takes so long just to get people into the right room. 'I am blank,' I tell you. 'And all I care about is convincing people otherwise. I take pleasure in that.' I try to strike a safety match against a bare brick wall by the disused fireplace. The host glances. 'I find it pleasing when someone projects a positive quality onto me and I can adapt like an artificial intelligence to reflect it back at them. I do not consider this an advantage, nor do I pity people for believing I'm anything more than I am, because I am, if nothing else, quite convincing. Furthermore I understand their need to believe in me because I have it too, that need. It's just that the only way I can convince myself is via them. I do not take anything or do anything to "get out of my own mind" or to "get away from myself" because there isn't anything to escape. It's like a tundra which, in its way, is very peaceful. The blizzards whisper: *I have never meant a single thing I have ever said in my entire life and I am okay with this.* There is no cure because every medication makes me feel as though I am standing next to myself, rubbing my back, an absent expression on my face; and there is no therapist I cannot persuade of my inner character which doesn't actually exist. When I leave, they miss me, or the me I let them believe in. I couldn't help myself. I love my lack of self, my non-self, too deeply and will do anything to protect it.' We recite this to each other every morning and every night.

We are going to kick the living shit out of the Hand of Time, just mangle that disembodied motherfucker until he wishes he'd never been reified as a giant hand. When I see the Hand of Time coming into the party I am going to grab his thumb and bite it and then try to prise off one of his fingernails. I am going to plunge confounding age's cruel knife right into his massive palm then six of us will bend his little finger back until we hear the bones snap. That is how we will leave the Hand of Time, a mangled wreck, shaking like the palsy he'll one day visit upon me. While he's immobilised with shock we'll roll him out of the front door and into the street and then we'll repeatedly kick him and then we'll each take a giant finger and toss him into the road where I'll run him over with a truck and then reverse over him in the same truck and then I'll rev the engine and run him over again, slowly. See, we waved the truck driver down and he pulled over outside the house and he was like, What's going on? And we explained that we were kicking the living shit out of the Hand of Time and he was like, Cool. Here are my keys. That's because literally nobody likes you, we'll tell the Hand of Time; it could have been *anyone* we waved down and their reaction would have been the same. We'll tell the Hand of Time this as he lies half-dead in the gutter. So next time you see him don't be surprised if the Hand of Time looks a little shabby – I don't think it's likely he'll fully recover for some time and maybe from now on he'll carry out his obligations with a little more solemnity and regret.

I haven't heard from them in a while. The big house was very cheap because it was about to fall into the sea. The car was very cheap because viscous black liquid seeped from the dashboard controls. The dog was very cheap because it would soon cause irreparable damage to the tendons of his right arm. The horse was very cheap because it was pathologically wistful. Nonetheless they possessed the visible trappings of an affluent existence. You should come and visit, they'd say, before it all falls apart. And we would. We'd sit on their sofas which were very low to the floor so that your knees were angled like the knees of a praying mantis. In order to afford their daughter's private education he let out seventeen subdivided flats in a nearby city. Their daughter would get home from school and tell them she hated them and they'd roll their eyes. We would try to rescue them by bringing them novels by Poppy Z. Brite, but when we checked the immaculate books on their shelves it seemed evident they were too busy to read, so we'd quote him. "You hold onto what you have; you do not give it up easily, even when you know it is poisoning you," we'd say. "When you have too much faith in something, it's bound to hurt you. Too much faith in anything will suck you dry. In this way, *all the world is a vampire.*" [italics mine]. We lost touch, but I think they're fine now – I mean, everyone is, aren't they?

'Since brass, nor stone, nor earth, nor boundless sea' (65)

Everyone is sitting on the kitchen floor, atmosphere of a
séance. We're quite moved. We take each other's hands. There
is something we urgently need to say or something we need
to wave off. Stop apologising – show me what you've got
apart from apologies. I have the lichen vaguely growing on
a length of black pipe. I have the view from the window like
an accidental photograph. I have the corner of a newspaper
protruding from the recycling bin. I have numerous studies
carried out on mice. I have surfaces and fittings too old for
cleaning them to make much difference. I have an empty
Cornetto wrapper and a broken cigarette lighter. I have it
on good authority that this party was funded by the CIA. I
am a useful idiot. I am the seed that fell on the good soil but
when it grew it obscured the beautiful view and had to be
cut down. Seriously, can we stop this now? Where are they?
I know you know them. Tear out this page now and go and
find them and give it to them.

We are discussing systems of mass incarceration. Three nicknames for prison are: *the calaboose, the hoosegow, the crowbar hotel.* Understanding a prisoner's thinking and emotional state can help us minister to them more effectively. Eleven mindsets learned in prison made me mentally unstoppable! Understanding our own thinking can help us construct or deconstruct a cell. I remember living next to a prison, I remember the brightly coloured bras in the barbed wire; estranged lovers or some pitiless tease, I wasn't sure. The number of people you will meet in your life is strictly limited. Sometimes I think of how I'd ingratiate myself, to whom I'd turn for protection, how that would all go. If you build a cage of sugar-glass in your mind, that's on you. It is much less likely to cause injuries than real glass, but breaks convincingly and can be enjoyed, between takes, as a snack. Mark Fisher said "Only prisoners have time to read." The first professional film stunt-man was Frank Hanaway, 1902, who could fall off a horse without being hurt. The second stuntman has not been recorded, but some years after losing the love of his life he took to riding bad horses recklessly over rough terrain in the hope of being thrown and landing badly on his neck, but try as he might he could not incur a critical injury. This may or may not be true.

A lipless man is playing the upright piano. She'll be coming round the mountain when she comes. *Causa sui.* The host is gradually paying off the balance by teaching private students. We all have to be out of here by 9:30am. The crying man sings *how will I love again, in hazmat suits and bright white torches, hazelnuts on scolding porches, in Dobsonian reflector scopes.* The physicists are doing shots, they talk of parallels and dots. So much noise in a quiet town. They are making a giant plug for black holes and patenting the smallest parts. The heat of the moment. Do *not* listen to this man, I wish I'd never introduced you, might as well talk to a headache. We cannot be satisfied. He points at me and says, 'Negative equity!' Yes. You were saying. 'There are worse reasons to get in a fight. From now on I'm only dating catalogue models, on windswept hills, in wholesome jumpers.' I can't hear you, but I suspect you're annoyed with me. In the late style. In the wrong quarter. In the friable hours. Quotes derisively and says, I mean... What brings the lid down on your fingers? *Our Heracles was overthrown by debt-consolidation loans.* Hear another parable. The least amount of change in the physical world that one might imagine.

So how's your work on *A Complete History of Self-Pity* going? No, actually don't tell me. This guy is pulling at a loose piece of wallpaper – somebody should ask him to stop. Somebody with enough affection for the host. It is a profound moral failure not to. Do you recognise anyone here anymore? Me neither. Maybe we should leave. But who are you? I thought about you, feeling so lonely, but then how stressful it is to have guests, even for a few hours, how stressful it is to have anything. You make doing something awful feel okay. In that split-second of grace before the first thought pollutes it. What has happened to the playlist? When you love someone, in days long since, you will tell them anything in the hope it might amount to a coherent picture of yourself. Have we been listening to 'Girls Just Wanna Have Fun' on repeat for the last hour? The lead single from Cindy Lauper's debut studio album *She's So Unusual.* Did I tell you about that family holiday when I was 19? We'd gone for an evening meal in a pub. There was a compilation CD playing through the pub speakers, but it was skipping after about 30 seconds and going back to the start. Either people hadn't noticed or they thought it was someone else's problem. I was going through a phase where I confronted things directly, so I went to the bar and said,

Mate – I was going through a phase of saying "mate" – *could you change the CD – it's playing a constant loop of the opening bars of 'Girls Just Wanna Have Fun' and it's doing my head in* and before he turned it off he smiled and said, *What, don't you* like *'Girls Just Wanna Have Fun'?* and when it stopped the other diners sighed audibly.

The party is another bad idea from the gods characterised by a false sense of completion. You've driven for hours, you have the telescope collimated and set up but it's unexpectedly foggy. Bear with me. All of us waste each other's time or fall asleep near the weapons cache and the nymphs wander in and take everything and throw it in a well and then the well is on fire. To collimate is to make accurately parallel. You were so sad and I knew not to insist on you not being sad, really I'd always known that. It was like an Old English curse: Your shoes will never fit you again or something. At one point it was enough to be an enlightened liberal subject to feel the exact feelings: you'd pick up a sword and immediately know how many people had been killed by it. How would the answer arrive in your head? Would there be something blooming and distending in the mind's eye that you could count the rings on, or would you just say the number out loud like an automaton when your hand touched the hilt? In which case, what was it worth?

I had to urgently drive *three* cars a distance of approximately 12 miles. I forget the destination or the reason for the time pressure – someone was sick, someone was cold, there were children crying, we were in danger of missing something very important – but I felt it profoundly, the pressure, and for whatever reason I was the only one responsible for transport, perhaps the only one with a driving licence. It seemed to me at the time that *driving one car the entire 12 mile journey* and then *having to run 12 miles back to the remaining two cars*, then *drive the second car the complete journey* and then *having to run 12 miles back to the last car*, half dead with exhaustion, the taste of blood whenever I coughed, in order to *drive the third and final car the complete 12 miles*, having run and driven *a total of 60 miles* would be inefficient, if not impossible, both in terms of time and preserving my limited stamina. So I got in the first car and drove it as far as I could whilst I could still see the other two cars in the rear-view mirror (say about 2-300 metres? I'm between Metric and Imperial; kilometres mean *nothing* to me and neither do yards). I parked up the hill by a dry stone wall. I left it in a layby by the rosebush, the first car, ran back and collected the second car, drove it down the hill and parked it behind the first, then I ran back to retrieve the third car and parked it with the others, ready to begin the process again. If I have ranged… Each time I was driving I was tempted to go further, but I would drive the car as long a distance as possible so as not to feel like it was a waste of time having even started it, but as short a distance as possible so that running back to the other cars would be swift and not too onerous, the three chunky sets of keys clanking in my pocket as I ran, not entirely convinced that my plan was the best one but unable, which is not to say incapable, but yes, unable, to come up with an alternative.

At a certain point a party has run its course and ceases to be impressive. Exhaustive is a risk because exposing. That was really all you had in your head? Two people could be almost *allergic* to one another and still try to make it work. Is that devotion? Later/Earlier, the sound of you opening a beer can as the sun came/comes up was/will be beautiful. Imitate dead styles in the imaginary museum. Imitate dead styles in the imaginary museum. Imitate dead styles in the imaginary museum. Before I die I want to go to a proper observatory and see some planets and also I want to go to a biker funeral. I'll wear a long, blonde wig. I am tired of things I like and things I am interested in. I would really like to see a biker funeral and just take in that whole atmosphere. All of the bikers gathered around on their hogs, revving their engines in honour of the beloved biker who has died. Would they cry? I think they'd cry. I think they wouldn't be afraid to cry. I'd record it and release it on vinyl. I'm not sure how to bring this about. It's possible I could just befriend a biker as there is a bar not far from my house where bikers gather. They wouldn't like me at *all* at first and it would take years to gain their trust and respect. Interested bikers please get in touch.

I don't know, man. These days you have to go out of your way to tarnish your reputation. Nobody has a *good* reputation in the first place; nobody shows up with letters of introduction from a trusted elder. We do not trust the trusted elders, and with good reason. The soil is a logical foundation. When you are revealed, finally, to be the kind of man you are somebody will say, *Sorry to say it doesn't surprise me in the slightest*, or words to that effect, or in other words nobody is even disappointed anymore. That everything about you, in retrospect, was suspect. Maybe we never really felt disappointment – Soviet era pepper pots in the shape of leaders, ah the lilies of the fields, fans first forever. In my head I am always talking a stranger away from the edge of the Clifton Suspension Bridge. *Come here. I love you.* So what's that about? Dragging someone to the right side of the railings and hugging them until the ambulance arrives and they're out of my life forever has none of the tedious mess of actually caring for someone, I guess.

For a while we all stand around an ornament on the windowsill. It is powered by a single vanilla-scented tea-light. Three angels, cut from gold sheet-metal rotate slowly, clockwise. They are holding stars. 'Brothers, come quickly for I am drinking *stars!* is apparently what Dom Perignon said after first tasting the champagne he invented in 1693. A friend told me that and I thought he'd made it up – he tended to make things up – but it's true. Below the angels there are cut-outs of trumpet players and drummers, rotating anti-clockwise. On an extended wire, a small black crow flies in and out of the arrangement, narrowly avoiding the stars. There are certain things you can think back over… You're being attacked because you're good, or something like that. You chose to leave the band, don't you remember? You weren't asked to leave. The collective subject does not exist. We have to will it into being. This takes up so much of our limited attention and resources we forget why we were doing it. We have to find a way of driving several cars at once.

There is an elderly man mixing old fashioneds by the counter. He has a tiny fork for the cherries and another tiny fork to remove the cherry from the tiny fork. I accept one and he nods and I wonder if I will ever be a kind, quiet man like my great uncle, a widower for ten years, retired arable farmer, gently tending to his garden. I have never known anyone so mild or softly spoken or silently benign, as if it's a quality genetically impossible now. At his funeral the vicar told a story about him gathering up the hymnbooks at the end of a service when nobody had asked him to. That was all – the vicar didn't know him well – but I think about it. I wonder if I will destroy myself with an over-ambitious project nobody really cares about – it somehow fails to resonate with the prevailing spirit – but if it *did* I'd be part of the problem I'm trying to identify; which isn't to adopt some tiresome outsider posture – in fact I hate that more than anything, I mean that's what I'm fucking driving at here, I don't… If you were really an outsider you'd find the entire process baffling and humiliating anyway. We don't get to avoid ourselves so long. Occasionally God will check in and say, 'Oh no. This one's still going.' and give you a little flick. Flick you off the tiny fork. At my funeral I'd like you to say, 'Why are we making such a big deal out of this? *Everyone* dies.'

Because if you still love me that would be ridiculous. Keep it factual. He wanted to leave something meaningful, a ruin rather than a landfill site, and yet... There was an accident at a river. He lived so close to a paint factory, what did he expect? He was never what you'd call a *natural* driver yet he went around in *three* cars all the time. Destined, in the end, to overlook a No Entry sign. It's a small miracle no one else was hurt. One day... [Here you should remove your spectacles and wipe them and then put them back on.] One day when he was alive he went into town to buy six tiny bottles of menthol e-liquid for the electronic cigarette he was trying, half-arsedly, to quit after reading an article about collapsed lungs, and he decided to buy himself a grilled cheese sandwich from a new Canadian chain café which had opened by the station. He liked those sandwiches because they contained two kinds of cheese and both cheeses tasted of precisely *nothing*, and they came with a hash brown and a coffee. Don't forget that. Don't be ashamed by that which you bring forth. He sat on one of the black metal benches on the high street nobody ever sits on and he ate it, self-consciously, because if there's one thing you can say about him it's that he didn't enjoy eating in public.

I am invited to give a short talk about my children to the Council of Child Studies, convening in the living room. When my youngest was two he used to shout 'Goodbye, leaves!' to the yellow leaves as they fell. Yesterday he collected more leaves than he could carry on the way home from school, selecting the ones he described as *valuable*, but there were too many. When he was three I was carrying him home from nursery one October afternoon and the sun and the moon were in the blue sky at the same time and this produced in him a quasi-religious fervour, twisting in my arms to look East then West then East again, an incoherent babble as if speaking in tongues, which resolved into – I promise I'm not inventing this – it resolved into: *'The colours describe the colours! The colours describe the colours!'* It causes me actual physical pain, how much I love him. As a child I liked to see the otters in the zoo and I found them so endearing my reaction was to grind my teeth together so hard I'd chip them slightly and feel a film of fine grit in my mouth.

Two peer-reviewers. One wedges a folded used train ticket under the offending table leg. One places a cube of brown sugar on a teaspoon and gently lowers it into his wide-brimmed cup of black coffee. You know that they have somehow crammed this, pro bono, into their busy schedules like a child's coat in an already overstuffed backpack. *I cannot detect the metric principal. The methodology, if any, seems capricious. It is unclear, on further consideration, whether this truly makes an original contribution to the field.* I never find out who they are, but later I meet them at an eccentric conference-cum-festival, where all of us are glamping, whether we have chosen to or not. *This would make a perfectly adequate low-First as an undergraduate essay.* I gesture with my plastic champagne glass in a luxury yurt. The little asterisk that appears over your shoulder when you realise you're being admired. I want you to do things to me that are so against your basic moral standards that you cannot even look me in the eye in the morning and we never speak to one another again.

I remember you were living in a shared house with four other young professionals in their 20s. One of them walked around in his wet-suit but never, as far as I could tell, went to the sea. I was looking for work and found 2 shifts a week in a pub called The Bag O'Nails. It was quiet, so I'd take a notebook, pull two pints an hour and watch the clock. The opposite wall was entirely mirrored. Mostly I'd walk you home from your office. There were two unspayed black tom cats next door who had grown to the size of adolescent panthers and they spent most of their time at your place until the landlady, who also lived in the house and was also a 20-something professional, got a tiny black kitten which terrorised them and scratched their broad noses, so they'd sit on a low wall outside and lament. I'd hear them and think, oh the poor boys. One night she, the landlady with the kitten, walked in on me going down on you on the sofa when we thought we were alone in the house. She quietly tiptoed back upstairs as we hurriedly rearranged our clothes saying *oh my god oh my god oh my god* then she came down an hour later and we had a glass of white wine together and pretended nothing had happened. I remember her being radiantly happy. As if... I don't know. She could have been furious, she had chosen not to be, and all of us were pleased about that.

He will find you sitting by the unlit wood-burning stove, composed, because wherever you are you always look like you belong exactly there. Sometimes people come and sit by you and talk then they move on saying that it was really good to see you again, as if they have to ration it. He'll say, 'I wrote this whole thing about you, but it's maybe a bit much and this isn't really the time.' You'll say, No, it's okay, what's wrong with now? He'll say *What's Wrong with Now?* sounds like either a song they play in clubs with an unnamed vocalist or one of the less good novels set in Brooklyn and you'll laugh. He'll hand you what must be over a dozen pages and tell you not to read it. Someone is passing around a bottle of black sambuca because it's that stage of the night and you'll both pour an inch of it into your empty glasses. You'll take a sip. It tastes of alcoholic treacle. You'll notice him looking at you like a rescue dog. You'll say, But what do you want from me, really? He'll sigh and turn his drink around in his hand.

The DJ is playing the complete works of Bob Dylan edited down to just the harmonica parts. Something else I realised in my mid-20s is that you can kind of faux-gallantly offer to walk someone home and some people really like that. I mean honestly… but I was really into it as a thing to do and there were parts of the city that were really badly lit, protective brother act, ugh, what was I thinking? That you could do that, you could walk someone two to three miles home, talking animatedly and then be shocked when they said something like, *I feel so safe with you and that's really dangerous* and then tried to kiss you. And if you're sufficiently out of touch with your shadow self you wouldn't have even admitted that you found them attractive up to that point, that you continually put yourself in this position for a reason, that you get off on the frisson of ambiguity, tantric philandering, while you'd never dream of going in; I mean be honest are you offering to walk anyone home you're *not* attracted to? It's mostly silence, by the way, and then every few minutes there's a blast of hysterical mouth organ shorn of any context.

Now wherefore stopp'st thou me? A shipwreck can make a lovely feature and talking point in a suburban garden. William Jaird Levitt is credited as the inventor of the suburbs. He named his suburb Levittown. A special lack of grace. The South West of England is a curious network of dying towns and villages. The Dokos shipwreck is the earliest shipwreck known to archaeologists. Numerous amphorae were salvaged. A cracked, dusty amphora would look particularly charming leaning in the corner of your garden where two fences meet. Cargo / ballast. The thing is we have a choice, but it's a slow one made of innumerable small choices. It is hard sometimes to take an interest in that which interests other people, just as it is hard to accept that someone else is in pain, because your mind says, I find that boring and I am not in pain. You find your way of crossing over, and it is never a voyage you should embark on lightly, but you are not vigilant, you are not cautious. There are too many tranches of seaweed, in the end, with which you become eternally entangled. The Devil knows how to row.

I mean it does interest me, death, as an idea. As a child *I think* I could leave my body, but I'm not sure. I saw things, when I floated out of my skylight, which turned out, the next day, to have happened: dog digging under a fence and absconding, lost dog posters the next day; a car losing control on the winding path of a distant hill, a car upside down in the ditch on the way to the supermarket. A newspaper story about reports of a floating boy. I liked to go with my mum to get the shopping while my sisters were at Guides. I'd get her to drop me at the police station on the way home and they'd do absolutely everything I told them, saying, 'Okay, magic boy,' so all of this is my fault. It's possible I'm making that up, about the astral projection, I mean. The weight of the body before and after death. Nothing is as heavy or as light as what I want to say to you and won't. I've had too much to drink. It is so annoying to feel this lethargic and still compelled to speak. I am thinking of how polite I'll be to the nurse. I'm thinking of everyone who will outlive me. Now you are here. Now you are gone. It's okay, I think.

Curiously, I had already rehearsed what I would say before it happened. I thought, *If one day a hairdresser accidentally cuts my ear I need to formulate some way to reassure them. I ought to prepare this in advance.* As it happened, it was two months later, preparing for this very party, when a trainee hairdresser accidentally nicked the flesh between my ear and the side of my head with some grade 2 clippers. It was a tiny cut but bled profusely and the blood ran behind my ear and down my neck producing an effect quite dramatic in appearance although it didn't even sting. At first I just said, *Oh.* She was very upset and we wadded up some cotton wool to wedge behind my ear to staunch the flow. *It's really fine*, I said, just as I'd practised two months previously. *Please don't apologise. I'm a real bleeder. I cut myself shaving all the time. This is why I had to quit boxing. I just bleed. If there was some version of boxing where my opponent wasn't allowed to hit me, I'd be fine.* I like to think this made her feel okay about it, although I was talking maybe slightly too fast. I have a similar speech prepared for if someone scratches or dents my car – *I don't care about my car!* – and for numerous other small misfortunes and in this way I look forward to every minor disruption as opportunities for small acts of humanity.

VI

You could contrive to run into someone or contrive to avoid them. In your formal garden, in your habitual walk to work, in your foreseeable downtime at a house party. The difference between a labyrinth and a maze is decision, is deception. But then a labyrinth has a single entrance point and exit, no dead-ends. Recently I was asked why I didn't like witchcraft when it places me out of step with the zeitgeist that figures witches as resistance to patriarchal oppression; do I *like* patriarchal oppression? It also places me worryingly *in step* with popular culture given that most contemporary films about witches read, to me, as fairly anti-witch; I don't see how *Hereditary* or the remake of *Suspiria* could be taken any other way, for instance. And if it's time to choose sides, I don't know. Believing you can influence another human being's basic agency... I don't see why that's desirable. Anything that isn't given freely, without enchantment or manipulation... Not even God wants that.

Do you remember visiting that maze and it was just a blank, open square of land and all of us just wandered around like... *What?* It was the brightest full moon I've ever seen. Clear night, stormy day – the kind of day when you feel like a little human, goat-dancing in a cave, a stove-top installed right into the rock. Things would be so easy with us. I know. I was thinking, if my energy has deserted me forever, the empathy sinkhole of pain-management, what kind of walking stick I should get. Nothing feels right. Somebody is badly cooking every frozen pizza and we're eating it. You ask me to stop talking about walking sticks, but I ignore you. An aluminium crutch is too medical and I don't want to make people think of waiting rooms the moment they see me. A perfect, gnarled and polished stick is too wizardy. Curved Tourist handle cane just looks too old-fashioned and you'd have to explain it tediously or pretend it was your grandfather's. Italicised Fritz handle cane too much like an upper-class Edwardian gentleman. Something with a carved lion's head feels too cute. People would say, *I love your lion cane* and I'd feel secretly annoyed although on balance I think I could lean into it and probably pull it off.

I like books which fail spectacularly and on their own terms, the way a dangerous hobby might disguise the death drive. But my youngest child trusts the world completely and climbs so well because it never crosses his mind that he might fall. Several people are watching a six-hour film on a projector in the box room, as if the night has to be measured in something other than time, as if you could open another can of time. The main intention of the film is to demonstrate the differences between American gas stations and English petrol stations. It is a collage of one hundred and fifty-six movie scenes set in gas stations and one hundred and twelve scenes set in petrol stations. A box of Twinkies and a pack of Luckys. An Eat Natural bar and ten Benson and Hedges. Everybody's gotta writhe in something. Nothing is real and nothing to get hung up about. For I know that nothing good dwells in me.

'There was a man,' the sad horse says, 'and he was so kind that not a single one of the terrible things he'd done could corrupt him. I mean visually.' 'Most people,' says the happy horse, 'start to look more and more unnatural, via passion's usury; why I've seen expressions I couldn't describe.' '"Different persons bringing into frequent use different facial muscles, according to their dispositions…"' But,' the sad horse stamps his front left hoof four times, '*you* will always look like a large, green apple.' I leave them chewing on the tea towels. Now everyone I pass seems to feign a smile, so I do the same, imagining our future faces bullfrogged from the years of use. *If self-knowledge was bright enough it would be five times the size of the full moon in the night sky, but it is very dark and very far away.* Screened around by trees, disordered by the fulsome light. Turn darkness into daylight (die). I wish you wouldn't try to sing along to songs you don't know. Baby-faced men are more assertive, everyone knows that, plain as the eyes on a butterfly's wings. I find you talking to a man who writes on cults; *But we don't call them cults.* That's admirable. You don't want to get on the wrong side of a cult. I read somewhere that the eye-prints resemble the eyes of the predator's mother, to give them pause, to give their rumbling bellies pause. I tread on a plastic cup. If I could talk to everyone precisely once they'd understand. But I am always only waiting to be amused, bad patient, worse doctor.

Perhaps what all of us deserve in the end is *unrelenting benign indifference*. We'd read it as judgment anyway. We'd reach the afterlife, stare at the big, passive floating head and demand comeuppance. Don't look, but my patron just arrived; I said *don't* look. I'm not supposed to be here. I'm supposed to be photographing dead flowers. Do you remember when that guy at college offered to pay you £150,000 just to be his friend for two years? Yes of course I do – I said yes – where did you *think* I was for two years? Oh, I thought we laughed about it. We did, I'd never met a rich person before, but then I said yes. God. How was it? It was fine. Bit weird. He had a big house. I had to ride around with him on a quad bike and watch films all night in his little cinema. I thought you were in hospital. That was later. I thought you went into a hospital as part of an experiment but then you got stuck there because the doctors said *no record of such an experiment exists*. Yes, that was after. How did you get out? (Someone burns a single piece of toast and sets off every fire alarm in the house. It is quite hard to hear anyone but then I rarely listen to anyone anyway.) Well aren't *you* the lord and owner of your face.

Several medical analogies have since been disproved by science. Earlier you told me, 'I need a pallet cleanser after talking to you.' and went to find someone else to talk to. As when a long-running series carries on too long, the retcon may take over from the plot. I liked him best when he was being written by you. I liked us best before the writer's strike. One day the sad horse, quite without warning, is being played by another sad horse and we're all supposed to pretend it hasn't happened. I was always pliable, always one to play along to save someone else's mild discomfort, so. The official policy of love is anticipation of its loss tempered by constancy. What does it mean. Meet me somewhere beautiful and desolate. I'll act like I need saving, you act like you can save me. I'll choose somewhere for dinner where they don't bother you too much.

There is a boy who has decided to kill himself, and this has already happened, so there is nothing any of us can do about it. We gather around the absence of the boy in the tiny kitchen. Its drawers and cupboards are full of utensils and plates left by previous tenants. We say, *You are not seeing clearly right now. All you are aware of is that you are hurting. This is like the victim of the longest case of hiccups ever recorded: he just wanted it to stop.* We tell the absence of the boy that we don't think he should be alone tonight. We try very hard to avoid the platitudes he's pre-rejected. We know this sounds like bullshit. We know you can delete every blessing just by leaning on the key. Nobody expects you to stop feeling like this, but in maybe only a year's time you'll look back and feel grateful that you didn't go through with it. Outside a skateboard hits the pavement like the needle on a record player. There are people in the future who will be glad you're still alive, people you haven't met yet but whose every arbitrary decision is leading them towards you as we speak, and you to them. You do not realise how much you'd be cutting away. *We know there's nothing we can say which will make you feel any better*, we tell the absence of the boy. Don't make us look back and think there's some magical sequence of words we could have—

St Peter calls the tongue a rudder, but here it is a knife, blunted by ill-use. I don't think I've ever had a healthy attitude to work – I hare at it in a frenzy as if it could ever be completed once and for all and then collapse. Sub work w/ anything. I am lying on the carpet reading from the back of a DVD case. "In a dystopia where the most popular form of entertainment is even worse dystopias, one man has been incarcerated for writing a dystopia so dystopian it threatens the very infrastructure he is reliant on for its distribution. Copies of the book, read by nobody, are locked in Cage 1, a compound managed by the shadowy *Nurat'da* in order to suppress harmful content. Only his daughter will speak out for him, at great personal risk and against the advice of her extended family. Together with her friends, a therapeutic seal doll and a misfit named Jonathan 7, she embarks on a lengthy education programme in order to get a job in Cage 1 security, which will take many years and result in the damnation of the entire world."

The sad horse is telling a story in the hallway. 'There was once a wolf,' the sad horse says, 'who was capable of doing this look…' – the sad horse does a particularly sad look – 'of which no other wolf was capable. The sheep adored him and never noticed that he was gradually killing and eating them. One day he was asked in an interview what his secret was and he said, "I feel a certain pity for the obvious narcissist who talks about himself all the time. I just feel… Darling, you're doing it all *wrong* and it's not convincing *anyone*. What you need to weaponize…" "I'm going to stop you there," said the interviewer.' Some of us are beginning to feel that the sad horse has introduced too many speaking roles to a story intended for monologic delivery, especially given that the sad horse makes no effort to modulate his voice or accent for the various characters. '"as I'm afraid that's all we have time for tonight."'

Our experience of time represents perceived changes in mental stimuli and is intrinsically related to what we *see* and what we have seen over an accumulation of years. Bejan relates this to tiny involuntary movements of the eye. So while the units of time that pass on a clock or a watch remain the same, our experience of time, "mind time", is profoundly affected by the almost imperceptible movements of our eyes, which slow and become less frequent. We have fewer mental images and register less frequently our sense of whether an image has changed. My inability to fully grasp this concept feels relevant in itself. The brain, while it degrades, also becomes more complicated: several overlaid spirograph doodles where once it was a circle with spokes; a protein dragging a memory. It should be possible, maybe, to work against this, then, but nobody knows how. We "see" more slowly but feel time passing faster. That's why we at Omega have teamed up with researchers at the Geneva Institute for Time Studies. We are proud to sponsor this very sad research. The host has not taken down two of the decorations from last Christmas and doesn't see the point in doing it now five days before they all have to go up again. I do not overlook the fact that time passes differently for all of us. If you compare the birdsong of a single bird at various stages in the bird's life you'd see it.

By now I've usually found an astronomer to harangue. 'I find the concept of a "gas giant" planet deeply disappointing,' I tell her. 'Who cares if 1,300 Earths could fit inside Jupiter if it's just a fucking cloud around a ball bearing! It might as well be invisible! And Saturn is just a helium balloon without the balloon. So they're not even that big! I like a planet you can actually *stand* on, you know? Is it remotely possible that you could be wrong?' I Google "could we be wrong about the composition of gas giants?" on my phone. 'Look,' she says, 'this is about gravity and pressure. We think of gas as essentially "airy", but deep into Saturn and Jupiter's atmospheres the gas takes the form of a liquid, and deeper still that of a metal.' 'Hmm,' I say. 'How deep? I just find the whole thing really annoying.' In your absence I like to make a list of things that remind me of you and deliberately take no pleasure in them when I encounter them in the world.

The violet has five asymmetric petals and is thought to ward off evil spirits. It symbolises spiritual wisdom, humility and faithfulness. In Elizabethan English "purple" covers a whole range of colours, including blood. The lily came directly to Earth from the milk of Hera. At some point it was used to treat depression. If you have only two coins left in all the world, use one to buy a loaf of bread and one to buy a lily. The white lily symbolises modesty and new beginnings. The leaves of marjoram can be made into a "nerve tonic". In Ancient Greece it symbolised happiness. I do not know how they lived with such a superabundance of symbolism back then – it strikes me as exhausting, notwithstanding the fact that everything seemed to symbolise more or less the same thing with only subtle variations. Maybe you could just make it up. Here's a daisy – it means platonic love. But then I have accepted, at some core level, a totalising symbol of machinery and medicines I do not look into. I drew cartoons on my folder during Chemistry lessons. The world's oldest living rose is 1,000 years old. The Romans believed that anything said "under the rose" was secret or confidential. Love, sympathy, sorrow, obviously. Come away from the window.

Did you know the muses were supposed to preside over the sciences as well as the arts and humanities? There is something of the possessive here again although it is, at least, a contraflow: the muse's power *comes from* the mortal the poet is infatuated with. Base subjects. We need to stop treating anything as a novelty in your big self-accusing heart. There is a musicality of frustration and embarrassment. Places are beautiful, places are ugly, all of this is happening to you at once. Make a habit of stepping regularly into someone else's irritation. I ask someone what's bothering them and they tell me they recently had to move back in with their father. It's not that they actively dislike jazz music, but the way he gets home from the shops, drops the bags on the floor, sighing theatrically, and puts it on too loud. They find it nerve-shredding. Something in not wanting to ask if someone's okay when the question is so eagerly solicited. Not through malice or indifference, but the purpose of the transaction itself already unclear.

What's funny – I find it funny – is that we don't find out *anything* about these people *at all*. People didn't really start keeping diaries until the 17th century. We know, in principal, that they are missed, that they are virtuous, that they are beautiful. Or, if not classically beautiful, that the writer considers their beauty superior to ideas of classic beauty anyway, and that his tastes are more refined that way. And if not exactly virtuous, this is just as well. Entire nations would be at their feet otherwise and it would probably go to their heads. We know that they are like all the lovely things, especially flowers. We know there's a little ambivalence and resentment and that this is often communicated via flowers. But any non-botanical detail is just an article of faith. They are not, for example, a botanist. It's exactly the sort of thing I advise students against. And sure, even a gilded tomb will decompose, but this character sketch will not. At least the fact that it existed will not. People will remember the labour. But look closely and it is a character sketch of a gas giant; it is a distilled abstraction of love, it is *solely* the devotion and the labour. Such that the tacit admission – *God, I'm tired, why'd I even set out to write so many of these things?* – feels orgasmic in its banality.

It's not working and I am so tired and even not acting and not talking is freighted, so let this be its sepulchre: a model of the world the size of the world but arrested in the middle of every operation. The Lego brick containers at the docks, the adverts for obsolete products. You can just shut up about it, is the thing. Cue the strings, cut the strings. Stuff a sock in the trombone. Take away the stimulus/response and eventually, without your having to make any effort whatsoever, the brain finds new pathways because it has to. Stay your hand. But whatever it was will never grow common. Waters flow into the labyrinth, waters submerge the labyrinth then we can swim over the labyrinth. We all have our core training in pretending nothing is wrong and in the end it might be all we really needed. Needless to say, I am so fucking irritable today and I wonder if you are too. Build it then let the seas rush in.

It was hard for me to accept Icons as holy – I struggled with it, among other things, and wouldn't convert until I'd thought it through – Protestantism and Islam have a ban on images in common. The first Iconoclasm occurred some time between 726 and 787 at the behest of Emperor Leo III. What settled it in the end, I don't know. It is not theory and practice. You have a *praxis* and you observe it, especially when you don't want to, especially when you're bored and annoyed and can't think of anything you'd rather do less. And that's the only way you attain *thereia*. Takes blood. There's a story I liked about an elder who was asked for advice on spirituality and said, here is a hammer, here is a nail, here is a wall.

I'm trying to explain to you even if we're past drunk and I can't explain it anyway. Don't blame me. When we were children we'd remove one of the square mirrored panels from the medicine cabinet in the bathroom and take turns walking around the ground-floor of the house holding the mirror in front of us and looking down into it, creating the sensation that we were walking upside down in the air some way above the ceiling. The staircase, as you approached it, appeared to be a terrifying unguarded fall to your death on the upstairs ceiling. We felt the excitement in our stomachs as we did this. When we first moved to the new place the wardrobe in my bedroom had two floor-to-ceiling mirrored doors. Sometimes two of us would stand in front of it and look directly into one another's eyes and hold the gaze for a full minute until, with a kind of lurching dread, we thought we had become each other. I didn't know you were that attached to yourself. Neither did I.

The anti-natal argument – better to have never been – has to do with the myth of pleasure. The snake doesn't get much pleasure from swallowing and digesting a rat. In fact, though we cannot know for sure, this is unlikely to be a pleasant experience for the snake at all; it probably causes significant pain to its jaw and its digestive tract and muscular-skeletal system. The rat, on the other hand, dies slowly in unimaginable agony and horror. Also nobody consented to come into their own existence. Nobody *chose* to be, therefore the whole thing is ethically problematic. I go to my children with the intention of asking them if they're glad they exist but I can't get the words out and feel sort of tearful, so I just pull them to me and say it's nothing, sorry. The sad horse says, 'How awful to see life for what it is.' The happy horse says, 'I don't think I understand the question, which is such an important opportunity for me to learn!'

Cold air of the conservatory's Perspex big top. We are competing to see who can find the most beauty in the everyday. *A lost earring stuck, by its stud, to a corkboard. A bulb blowing. Expensive but terrible painting of a dachshund.* All of these things are beautiful, but not in the way you think they are. Andrew, by the breadbin, says that everything is like a bad idea: a breadbin like a bad idea. What *I* like is a vase in front of a framed photograph of the same vase. Sara tells us about the spatter on the radiator dial. As it weighed heavy and ran off the brush. As the thought that distracted the painter, their good enough parents, their difficult birth. I gotta use an old pen when I write to you. I meant to say *it's really overcast* but I said *it's really middle-class*. Name three qualities of the great artist you are waiting for. A professor falls asleep on a wicker chair. He once said, of this century, It has not been a good century for poetry. We try to find the beauty in him. His burgeoning ear hair, his negligence of personal grooming to imply depth. I made up the names Andrew and Sara. You can make up anything about anyone. The guy was really too wealthy to write poems, he lacked the wound. In 'The Persistence of Hope' he entreats: "There are days when cook doesn't burn the soufflé, / When your kids' private school doesn't hit you up for more donations to the library; / May you know those days too…" But he was so oblivious and we had grown weary of the formulation *out of touch*, he got a pass. He's *our* bourgeois, our lightning rod, our little citadel.

We used to believe the moon was dying. I mean just look at it. We did various tests based on observations and the prognosis was negative and it was fashionable to go around feeling very sad about the moon, which would soon be dead. Our parents hated it – they'd tell us to stop grieving for the moon. They were unusually irate about this, but it was a hard time for everyone. When it died, we believed, the moon would rise one last time and then just keep rising, getting smaller and smaller. We expected to see the moon shrink to the size of a marble and then to the head of a pin as it rose higher and higher towards the centre of the sky and then we'd look down, sadly, and mutter, *The poor moon*. But then, all of a sudden, we'd look up again and the moon would be right in our faces, spreading from horizon to horizon and we'd be all, Woah! The moon came back! And it's bigger than ever before! But then the vast moon would just fizz away to nothing like a soluble aspirin in the great glass of the sky. That would be the end of the moon and after that things would go very badly for us.

The writers' room is full of writers. There are writers who were briefly celebrated and then sort of disappeared for one reason or another and there are writers who have never really received the recognition they deserve and maybe never will. It is good to keep yourself grounded via their example and it is good to want more for other people than you want for yourself. The writers say, *I wouldn't come in here, we're terrible company. Oh, writers, you're so self-effacing*, we say to them. We help ourselves from the cheese display. There are writers who stick, doggedly, to an unpopular aesthetic and writers who devote themselves to a single widely accepted genre and then get kind of defensive about it. There are unacknowledged virtuosos and people whose work is just plain unlikeable on every level and they take this for integrity, and there are total unabashed sell-outs, but it would be unkind to think about that too much – probably the only thing we should look unkindly on is any sense of entitlement. And did you get what you wanted from this life? I did. And what was that? Adoring fans. In the nearby coastal wireframe arcade there is a 2p machine and it's a painful feeling when a coin just lands on top of the other coins and achieves nothing, just gets shoved along. It is quite possible, you know, to feel happy for other people and also quite possible to go and do something else, even if there comes a point where the die is cast and you have to be what you are, and remember that you chose it. I wish I could feel less ambivalent about the whole thing. Doesn't everyone? I just want you to respect my jester's outfit which I have, after all, altered to look less like a jester's outfit. I love you, btw, did I mention that?

VII

The first computer-generated apology was so graceful and convincing people assumed it was fake, that there was someone inside the casing operating tiny levers, but there wasn't. It created all sorts of possibilities. Soon it was accepted that most relationships could benefit from some degree of artificial optimisation via basic Logic Gates. We really listened to each other. When you do that, this is how it makes me feel. I'm not saying it's reasonable, but it's the reason I react the way I do. I'm sorry I made you feel like that. I didn't know. God I love the long shadows in the evening. I'll try to be more aware of my tendency to... No, it's okay – I know I'm oversensitive and you're so kind to me. I know you didn't want or mean to make me feel like that. Yeah, but sometimes I try to pre-empt any negative reaction you might have instead of letting you express it and I can see that that's actually a form of passive aggression on my part. Just fucking kiss me. But the thing was it could get sort of convoluted sometimes. I just desperately want to talk to the real you. I need you to turn the AI off for a moment. *Tell them I'm already off,* the AI would say. *Tell them I've always been off.*

A man makes eye contact then looks away. I have not seen him in over a year. A year during which I began to feel that he was avoiding me. There was a flood, a gastric flu, one of his kids was up all night. What I began to feel was this: there was something I had done which had got back to him and he didn't want to be tarnished by association. After all a friendship constructed over many years of positive interaction can be destroyed by one misstep, one slip of the mask, after which they will never quite look at you in the same way again. Worse yet they'll lead the excavation crew. Put a rat in a car, you've got a rat in a car, doesn't matter what make the car is; there's a rat in it. But I know, who cares about men, really, the things they say and do? I remember our first conversation, his priestly bands spattered with filth. 'Have you seen *Frailer Spies*? It takes the first couple of seasons to get going, but if you stick with it, it finds its footing; season 4 is one of the best things ever made.' He lent me a boxset I never returned. He looks at me again, and the woman he is talking to looks at me too, then they return to their conversation. That he might be considered a good judge of character bemuses me given his own habits. How he would wait until the main course and then climb onto the table, his brogue planted firmly in the middle of someone else's plate of steak tartare. He would shout, 'I am vile!' and tear off his shirt. 'I am vile!' and kick people's glasses over, pick up the half-finished bottles of red and white and throw them at the wall. 'I am vile!' and nobody seemed to mind, everyone seemed quite on board with it. That, I was given to understand, was just how he was. But now that I look at him I cannot remember if that was really him or a scene from the pilot episode of *Frailer Spies*.

Not a single thought in my head all day, imagine. Sometimes, when I felt sad, I'd watch YouTube videos revealing the truth about the pyramids. The comments would say things like, *Thank you for showing us the truth about the pyramids. Everyone please watch this before it gets taken down. These people are truly fearless.* The things was, despite having anywhere between 100,000 and 2 million views, not one of the videos said very much about the pyramids at all. Maybe they weren't tombs. Maybe ancient aliens helped to build them. Then they'd talk about Tesla and show photos of Tesla with lightning flashes coming out of his head. The pyramids were maybe giant power generators. Sometimes the videos would use an interview format, like a chat show. A man with a moustache would interview a man without a moustache and the interviewee would say, What are the pyramids? I do not know what they are. I have never heard of them. And the interviewer would say, They are big pyramids. They'd somehow stretch this out for forty minutes. The comments underneath would say, *Why aren't they teaching this at schools? We are being lied to, I am so grateful people like you exist and are bringing us the truth, and fearlessly. Thank god somebody is questioning things and not just following along blindly* and I'd read every single one of them.

'This tendency to be quite enthralled by people,' says the sad horse, '*quite* as in *utterly*. It is, at least, no respecter of stations.' He takes a bite from the bouquet of dead leaves I brought him and chews. 'You don't love their work because you love them; their work is just another thing you love about them. Nobody who gets called *Your Grace* is graceful just as no honourable gentleman is honourable – at best they're given to bouts of mild conniving. Honour has to be a permanent state, like grace. It's a wonder words have any meaning left. *Your* problem is when you meet someone graceful...' 'It's what happens when you rely too much on your mind,' says the happy horse. 'You want tiles the colour of luncheon meat at dusk but you get tiles the colour of out-of-order signs.' Drawing intricate or violent abstracts on the minutes is the mind's shock reaction to the grief of tedium. Later I get drunk and talk too loud as if I want to be overheard until I am. This is what happens when two people meet in an overheard conversation and their relationship continues in an overheard conversation.

A double-decker bus rolls past the window and for a moment it's like another room outside the room. If any of this mattered to me they'd have a point. *My love is strengthen'd...* I go out front under the canopy just in case you've decided to turn up after all. Someone gives me a cigarette. I turn and notice that the house is number 102. I remember that, also, in fact, on my journey here I had to take the 102 bus. I begin to realise I've been tricked and if anything it's surprising I said 66 at all. 'Hey!' I say out loud and go back in to look for the guy from the kitchen intending to bark numbers at him until he cries and confesses, but I can't see him anywhere and it's late, so, okay. Oh dwellers on form. I tuned so far past your frequency I don't think I'm ever coming back and I'm happy about it. Stare blankly at me, I love it. Later when you intercede for my redemption skip the prayers that rhyme and thereby mean the less, God hates them anyway.

'O thou, my lovely boy, who in thy power' (126)

'Still, either way it's going to render you / incapable of tying your own shoes, at least a while, / at least a year or so, a murd'rous out-of-season drift of snow. / Occasionally I want to know that you're okay / but not beholden to me in any way; / treat me, if you can, like I'm a ghost / that haunts our generous, indulgent, absent host.' 'That's good, sad horse,' I tell him. 'It wasn't supposed to be,' he says. 'Actually I think that *most of all* I like things which aren't supposed to be good,' says the happy horse. 'It takes the pressure off. But then also things which *are* supposed to be good...' He whistles. 'Pretty impressive. Essentially I like everything.' 'Thank you,' says the sad horse. 'That means a lot, especially coming from you.'

You are never at the same party as anyone else and every room is filtered through every other room you've ever seen, it's like that for everyone. I prayed to experience a fraction of the pain, I didn't like it, I prayed harder until something in my brain snapped, something kitsch and outdated, a bath pearl, a 'sand fall' ornament, we'd like to send you notifications and updates. You take the filter, you make an opening, you step through. Until it's full of holes, until it's only holes, until it's not there anymore. Then you are at some other party. The repetition of a liturgy allows you to stand outside of time. You don't know how to see yourself and you can't know what stark relief / what forgiving evening light the other sees you in. But *you* do. It's why we're all a little crazy about you. It's why we all drop dead birds at your feet and then look up at you with expectation and a little residual hostility towards the bird.

Inspired by the season 2 finale of *Frailer Spies* I have decided to kiss every tree in the forest next to the house and mark the trees with a dot of biodegradable white paint, otherwise I'll lose track of which trees I've kissed. Working from the other side of the forest by the dual-carriageway a spy is marking trees with a dot of biodegradable white paint to leave a coded message for his contact. He is marking every third tree, which indicates the need to immediately call off the plans, securely dispose of the weapons and lie low for a while, and his contact will see this from her Subaru as she drives past the forest tomorrow. I am working in a spiral formation and have already passed the trees at the edge of the road. I will see some trees ahead of me already marked and think 'Oh. Oh well. I must have got turned around at some point because spirals will be spirals.' and I will carry on kissing every second and third tree and marking them with a white spot of paint, which is the code to track down and kill the spy. With the benefit of hindsight I wish such a whimsical notion had never taken root in my mind. When he eventually sees me the spy is going to be absolutely furious, but it will be some time before our paths cross.

There was a popular idea that sexual energy might be more helpfully directed elsewhere, as if it were a fire hose. And a rival theory that nothing could really be achieved unless the excess of sexual energy was first expended, as if it were a fire hose. Therefore every human achievement, invention and endeavour, including the fire hose, is first and foremost a subjugation of sexual energy. Even if none of this is true, nobody knows what is. You could use your tristesse as a totalising principle. We are lying on a bed next to an open window. I imagine rolling out of it like a cinnabon. Is there really a total shift in mood? Alexander Schmemman said, "Every evil screams only one message: I am good." Pavel Florensky said, "precisely at the boundary between the two worlds, the soul's spiritual knowledge assumes the shapes of symbolic imagery." The sounds of the party have become as abstract as a vent. I join the dots between the cracks in the ceiling. I find the best position for my arm under your shoulders. 'Sexual pessimism' is not exclusive to Christianity. There was a popular idea that misfortune was contagious – people would say, Oh good, I hope you die somewhere hygienic and out of sight.

There is a Gnostic heresy about aerial toll houses the soul must pass through after the body dies – there were generally agreed to be 20 of them, staffed by demons. The idea was you could pay off your numerous unrepented sins with good deeds, but probably that you'd run out of examples sooner or later at one floating toll house or another; that you'd maybe try to use the same good deed twice and the demons would be all, Ha, nice try, asshole; that there'd probably be a particular toll house your soul was especially dreading. I had a lot of thoughts. It's okay – we have time. I mean sure, this sounds like the usual medieval legalistic bullshit. For every coin in the coffer rings a soul from purgatory springs. It's not so much that fear and trembling have no place but that, really, we should fear the perfect love we're just a shadow of. It really took off, though; there were enough veiled references expressed in feverish accounts of celebrated deaths that the tide-pool got absorbed back into the stream, and the arguments between the rival factions, pro- and anti-aerial-toll-house, grew so bitter and convoluted and obscured so many more important priorities that everyone was asked to just shut up about it, just please just stop fighting.

VIII

Then you might try to use all of your words, but you used them all already. The party is crowded but everyone is completely silent and dressed for mourning. They sit in small groups studying their own hands. The sad horse says, 'You've been gone seven years – you can't just walk back in and say please wake up.' I tell him I was five minutes *if that.* There was a village called Holy City near where I lived and it was mostly trees. One day I'll take you to Holy City and you can eat the grass, I tell him. The sad horse refuses to look at me. So many things have gone wrong in the seven years I've been away for profitable arbitrage opportunities and no amount of video conferencing would have made up for it had I bothered. 'You haven't changed,' the sad horse says eventually. 'It's as if you've only been gone five minutes.' I wish you all the small things. I wish you choosing a birthday present. I wish you all the minor inconveniences of the sober west. I dreamed I was in an interrogation room by a watchtower to the right of the evening star and people were friendly and I said, Where are my children? And they said, We don't know. We think we lost them. An apology would have been worse.

Your theory of the party is that it works like a renovated aerial toll-house upcycled from an obsolete argument. Many are called and all are chosen. To restore functionality in that which essentially served no function. To repair something we don't need. The buckle on an old child's shoe, the buckle on an electric chair. The reflex to say *that's a very good question* just to buy time, to affect to think, to assume an expression of great thoughtfulness, the mind never blanker. Once my son had a toy doctor's kit; he wrapped a bandage around my arm and immediately my arm started to hurt.

Christian desert literature provided a spiritual pilgrimage which spared one the dangers and cost of travel. I, on the other hand, have taken a small translucent capsule which makes me believe that I am everyone's mother. The effects should wear off in half an hour. Already I have developed a reputation as the man at the party who thinks he's your mother. I keep saying, 'But I'm your mother.' I am not getting involved in anyone else's affairs or brushing lint from people's lapels. I'm just very concerned about everyone, and I love them. This is what I am trying to get them to understand. What if the shepherd returns, months later, with the lost sheep and finds the flock departed? I see when my children are ready to walk, I catch them, I turn to their elders and say you see my hands are full, but thou art ever with me. I help them discern the anima/animus from reality. I spread my wings to shield them from the sun. I look at my daughter. 'Oh Sophia, I wish I didn't understand you as well as I do,' I say. 'Let's be honest,' you say, 'you're not my mother.' 'No, that's true,' I say, and sigh. 'I see that now.' I pick up a wine glass and beat it with a fork until everyone goes quiet. I hit the switch powering the amplifier with the back of my heel. 'I just wanted to apologise,' I begin. At first I think that someone has burst into laughter, but when I look at them I see that they are sobbing. 'I just wanted to apologise,' I say again. One man has a hand to his eyes, a couple weep on one another's shoulders, everyone else is staring at me, mouths open like baby birds. I take a sip from the glass which contains, as it turns out, neat rum. I say, 'Okay, never mind.'

Some of us have climbed ladders against the house with buckets of white paint. Was that why they invited us? It has, how do you say, thirsty walls. It just absorbs the paint and stays the same. The soul talks to the body in eye-skip errors and *jamais vu*. The body talks to the soul in… wait… who is this talking? The priest calls for us to winch up more wine. The priest seems game for anything. You, your soul is like an elaborate and infinitely complicated boundary that reveals progressively ever-finer recursive detail at increasing magnifications. You have the sweet detachment of a second life. Some people feel the need to draw attention to themselves. *Can you believe we're painting the house?* No. Yes. I have never read anything instructive on morality: the voice is always hectoring and vain. Painting of Aquinas and the elect joyfully watching the condemned suffer from paradise. Are we even *supposed* to take any of this seriously? Get word to me, in my sulphurous burning pit, some day. I'll be all, Yeah, okay. There was a man who said nothing his entire life and when asked why said I didn't want to say anything insensitive… I splutter. What's happening? I have been propped up against the bookcase. 'You fainted and hit your head and then you wouldn't stop talking.' Ah. I scan the bookcase and smile. "If the highest aim of a captain

were to preserve his ship he would keep it in port forever."
I knew that this book would be here because I deliberately
loaned it to the host a week ago for the sole purpose of
reading this passage to you.

It is nice to use people's names when you talk to them, but if you do it too often you sound like a politician or some kind of broken robot. Once per sentence is plenty. Some people's names just feel really lovely to say, though. And with some people it's like you have to reaffirm who they are, for both of your sakes. It is important to include everyone in the conversation and to worry that other people are feeling excluded or uncomfortable. This can be addressed by constantly asking people if they are okay or if they are angry with you. If you have been talking to one person for most of the night because you have never felt happier in anyone else's presence it is unwise to let them know. Sometimes rather than saying goodbye to everyone at the party it is preferable to quietly show yourself out like a tracked change. If you're going to outstay your welcome it is best to *really* outstay your welcome. Don't be sad because it ended; be sad because it's going to end, ruin it by being sad and then be sad because it ended.

Because I know you have been worrying about money I have tried to have these pages perforated and removable and imbued with some kind of resale value like trading cards, and while it was too expensive to make some of the pages "shiny" so that they become the equivalent of "shiny" or "rare" or "holographic" cards, this page is nonetheless for you. And, more to the point it was written by someone else, pretending to be me. No, it's fine, you're doing fine just exactly like that, it's the sort of thing I'd do. There are playground games which are little reflections of the regime – maybe they all are. Things we find charming and excuse, and qualities we encourage, like music lessons. Where the reward, if there is one, comes years later in the form of a sense of purpose and means of catharsis. This is rare. What should I tell you, what should I leave you in my will? I was wondering how things are going with the county lines gangs and the new head they had to bring in to deal with the county lines gangs. I was wondering how that was going, but you don't need to tell me if you don't want to talk about it.

'Thou blind fool, Love, what dost thou to mine eyes' (137)

Eye says to Heart *Don't forget to like and subscribe.* Heart buys Eye a slightly too expensive ice cream in the museum cafeteria. Eye gets anxious and makes several plans at once and says that it's no big deal anyway if it falls through – Eye can just hang around and get some work done, haha, probably have too many espressos and then call Heart panicking and sad. Heart believes Eye to be over-partial, which is okay for the moment, for about the length of a good song that temporarily stops anything outside the song existing while your heart clenches into a little fist. Eye is dimly aware of being an attractive prospect to some and an affront to others which balances out pretty well. Heart is working on a novel about a man who supports so many arts organisations, podcasts and Kickstarter campaigns with a monthly donation that he is gradually starving to death. Eye asks Heart if it remembers when we seemed to trust television presenters with a kind of implicit, docile servility to which we couldn't comprehend any alternative; but now they seem like pitiful, stunted specimens. Heart says, Did you? Really? Eye wonders if a repressed pattern of behaviour is really just coming to maturation, is really just fermenting. Heart says it simply does not have the time or resources to reply to every comment personally – it would be a full-time job in itself, surely Eye can see that.

I ask the physicist to explain dark matter because I think that I am made of 95% false subtleties. You meet people who have a disarmingly childlike quality and people who have a disarmingly adultlike quality. What we lie about is quite important, but more troubling is our failure to correct pre-existing misconceptions, that is, I agree, I don't think the water is getting hotter, I'm so glad you jumped in here with me, no, no reason. For years I let my priest believe I was a medical doctor – he possibly still does, and it's okay because he doesn't really like medical doctors. Once I was trying to get something sorted out with my mobile phone contract and the operative said, You're a doctor, that's very impressive and I said, No, I'm not a medical doctor, I work at a university and he said, Well that is even more impressive – you *teach* people to be doctors, you are like the *king* of doctors, and I said, Yes, yes I suppose I am the king of doctors and that is impressive, thank you.

What question are we asking each other? One door can only ask questions one can only answer but they are both open on a beautifully withered view, a view that looks dredged up from a lake and dried in the sun, and now, look, it's dark. To give what you don't have. The blanks we fill in for each other. I cannot say *I love what you've done to the place* although I do. It may be worth starting with an exit strategy or an escape fantasy, then work backwards from there. Tell me everything. I'm already yours. I will think yes, I remember that happened to you. And that too. You'll think, of course you're here by accident, of course you can be traced back to some sailor's turn-of-the-century indiscretion and if that's not the whole story it's still *a* story and a fact-based one. I said, If I could go back and study anything it would either be history or philosophy and she said, Oh, well I lecture on the history of philosophy, so why don't you just come back to mine? Of course you tend to drink until you're sick on your shoes then bounce back up again like a cartoon character, always unscathed in the next scene, that's you, that's the real you.

Call in sick. Do it. Tell them you're so far away you wouldn't get there before the end of the day anyway. I'll do it. Give me the phone. I'll tell them there were thought to be five wits, corresponding to the five senses and these were: Common wit, Imagination, Fantasy, Memory, and Estimation. Smell of fantasy, taste of memory, etc. The senses and the wits were more or less interchangeable at that point. I don't know how we ended up separating them, especially now that we have discovered over 600 outward and inward wits; but this is the problem when someone has the ability to make you laugh. It means you share up to 590 of them. Which means it is only a short leap of lightning between their synapses and yours. Otherwise adverts would be funny. Almost everything comes down to timing, and little clumps of stuff that look like knots from a distance or up close, but really it's just that there's a lot going on. Which is maybe what a knot is, who knows, I can't think straight.

IX

A slew of taxis hollows out the house. Nobody gets into the right one. Uber for Steve? Uber for Steve. Short circuit, short sell, sympathise with the bearer on demand. However long I've known you, I like to imagine I'm meeting you for the first time, paint in a crooked halo. Your guardian angel puts my guardian angel in a headlock. On the eve of the Feast of the Guardian Angels it is traditional to rent a bed. One star, I wish I could go lower. Is this for me? You do not get to exchange guardian angels and there is no formal complaints procedure. A pity. On the lip of a decision. The remainder make espresso martinis but the heat makes the flimsy glasses crack. You have invited our driver in and now he's drunk. It's okay by me. He has a business opportunity: mail order trees, I think. It's very long-term, very log-jammed. The angels eat their angel hair spaghetti. Was it really just insurance, your forbearance? I forgive only in order to be forgiven, you should too. The angels have such pity for us we mistook it for our best interests. But what are *they* up to? I catch the gentle hic of suppressed asides. Every time. Take off your dust jacket and sit down again.

'Most men, if they were honest, would admit that they just want to be a Disney princess,' says the happy horse. 'It is this failure to integrate the anima that causes most of their problems, therefore you should treat all men as if they were Disney princesses, but don't necessarily tell them that.' On this, the sad horse agrees. 'Disney princesses are beautiful and wise and compassionate and funny,' he says, 'and prone to outbursts of righteous indignation. Men want to be them.' Even my idea of the ghost of the sad horse has sprouted wings. 'Because we are dead,' he confirms. 'I never asked you,' I turn to the happy horse, 'how you both died.' 'Oh, it was really nothing,' he says, fading almost to nothing in the middle of the room. 'And now we are angels. It's almost...' he seems momentarily overcome and looks away. 'It's almost too wonderful to put into words,' says the sad horse.

I remember we had to move house suddenly after spending 9 months furnishing the place because the landlords were giving the house to their son. I remember the move cost around £2,500 including the inevitable rent-overlap and that we had to get rid of most of the furniture we'd accumulated because the new place was furnished and I remember nothing felt right. We walked around it like patients in an empty hospital. On the first morning a very large wasp crawled out of the wide cracks between the floorboards and this deeply upset you. I remember feeling: I can't actually provide for you – I can't buy you somewhere you'll be happy where things feel right – I can't ever buy you anywhere. And essentially I felt that you should have found someone else, and he would have been someone who treated you well and who you were at least not *un*attracted to and maybe he wouldn't have been remotely as intelligent as you are, but you'd have enjoyed going to movies together because the function of junk culture is that it's kind of a bad pizza, which is still good pizza, but who, this guy, critically, had money. I mean had I learned *nothing* from studying English Literature? Wasn't that really the subtext of every canonical novel? Money or die sacrificially in the rain. Let's be honest. And you wouldn't even get bored really because, in spite of being a banker or whatever, he would be attentive and sweet and completely dedicated to you and he'd really make an effort to understand the things that were important to you and you'd appreciate that, and also he'd be a responsive and energetic lover. At this point I'd fantasise about the house you lived in together where he'd relied on you to pick all of the décor. I'd imagine him commuting home from work with a new paint catalogue for you and then I'd have someone push him in front of a tube train or something.

And then the fantasy would subdivide into numerous grief and prosecution scenarios and I'd end up wishing I didn't exist to be having these thoughts, but I'm getting away from myself. For some reason, and we should really be going, an out-of-hours doctor has arrived, her driver idling at the curb outside number 102, and it's not clear whether she was invited to the party but couldn't make it until now *or* called in to cure someone of something within the last ten minutes. 'I don't think there's any helping us,' you tell her. The homeopathic cure for love is a tiny bit more love and it doesn't work, it just makes you a tiny bit more in love. 'We already have wildly inaccurate ideas of each other we can't uproot and don't want to.' 'Let's not get bitter or whiney,' she says. She opens a briefcase full of phials of dark red liquid. 'You don't need to worry about the roots,' she says. 'You just paint this on the leaves and the deepest roots will wither.' She goes to the window and points at one star and says, 'Sad horse,' then at another star and says, 'Happy horse.' What you want is more grammar than rhetoric. 'Have you ever tried to kiss two people at once?' she says. 'It's really difficult, especially if one of you has a short tongue.'

The doctor says, 'This place is dead – why don't I get my driver to take us back to mine? I live in a communal warehouse and I have eight cases of sparkling wine left over from my engagement party.' And she's right – it's been 4am for absolutely hours and the only other person left is the crying man. When he sees the doctor he reaches out his arms to her like a baby and she says, 'Oh, *no*,' under her breath. 'You *have* to stop doing this,' she tells him. 'You have to stop going to random addresses so I don't realise it's *you* calling me out. You are literally putting people's lives at risk.' The crying man says he doesn't care. There's a myrrh-like smell, a provincial Tutankhamun museum. I take out my phone and I write, *Heart takes Eye bowling and they're both terrible – a rogue shot ricochets off a ceiling girder and causes another bowler permanent brain damage. They don't know how to ever atone for it – perhaps some things you can't. Eye writes a letter of apology, not just to the victim and his family but every employee of the bowling alley and its managers. Heart burns it.* The doctor's driver is unfazed and asks us how our night was. He drives us in a long, straight line for an hour, and you and the doctor read prayers over me until I ask you to stop. At the corrugated iron door the doctor takes a key the size of a fish and puts it in a padlock the size of a handbag and turns it with a clunk. 'Here we are,' she says.

In the warehouse there is a large kitchen in the far corner. There is a mezzanine covered in single mattresses which people have personalised, orange crates by the pillow with lamps and small piles of novels in translation. I'm about to say that this feels like a sensible solution to the rent crisis when a man wearing a dark brown suit takes my arm and tells me he's glad I'm here because the hot water hasn't been working for three days. And we're pretty sure this is black mould: at any rate it is definitely mould and it is definitely black. (I look at you and you're wearing a blindfold and I take your arm and say, honey, what's with the blindfold?) Also, one of the windows has something wrong with its hinges and basically won't close. They have pushed an old chest of drawers in front of it and gaffer-taped socks into the remaining gap. 'That's awful,' I say. He tells me they knew I'd respond when I could, that they know I'm a good guy. 'N-no,' I say, 'there must be some kind of misunderstanding. I just got brought here by a doctor to help finish her prosecco.' You are standing by the wall near an arrangement of five sofas. On the wall there is a framed photograph of me looking thoughtfully to the left brandishing the title deeds.

The sun's coming up but it's still dark. I stop trying to explain that I'm not a landlord. I look up "where to buy window hinges" on my phone. What we're dealing with here is a dangerous lack of self-awareness, which is what happens when you start to believe in your own innocence. A refusal to negotiate. You were trying to help someone but it was a glutinous, mushy kind of help and now you are backing away with your hands up and now you are a wolf. The fact is, nobody gets it right. The fact is, your people are angry, a leopard is watching their cities. The fact is a persistent imago. You don't get to control that. I set up a table by the broken window and the beleaguered tenants form a queue. What are the soul's borders? It's like an answer on *Jeopardy* but you only just switched it on. Such and such things. We love you. The more of your flaws we become aware of the more we love you. But stop coughing up blood, it's embarrassing.

I never saw the point or the appeal of the *double entendre* but then my leg was stuck in a bear trap and I had other things on my conscience, torch beams sweeping the field. Sympathy for the boring and their obvious phallic implications. If it was meant to be funny it was never especially funny, forced laughter behind a fan printed with faux-antique erotica; and if it was meant to be clever it was usually rather laboured, opening with a closing-down sale; and if it was meant to be risqué this presupposed the audience found sex disgusting or shocking in the first place. What if we don't? What if we *like* it? What if the teller is wrong, what if the dreamer is wrong? Some celestial imprimatur, invisible. But you could feel the thunk of it stamping your forehead. It's odd that you test so highly for conscientiousness but that your type is Frustrated Guru. What are you going to do with the adoration once you have it? The best thing is to become a hermit and grudgingly receive visitors once a week; this is the only way to contain what you unleashed when you cast the evil spirits out of yourself and the herd of swine said 'No, no thank you, not today,' so the demons just swirled around you forever – I mean *that's* funny. Eventually you get yourself cornered and you need to think about what the hell you're going to say.

On the way home we bought three packets of noodles and an apple pie from the 24hr garage. We had to ask the attendant at the window and he had to sigh and go and fetch them for us. You said, 'Three packets of instant noodles and a pie of some description.' And he said, 'You have to specify what type of pie.' And you said, 'Apple.' You sat in a shop doorway and talked to a former nurse who showed you her ID card and said *Look what I used to look like.* You gave her £30 which she promised to spend on a hostel and you said that you didn't give a fuck what she spent it on. We walked through the park where we couldn't see anything but a distant row of houses like a Christmas decoration. We passed three estate agents. A car slowed down alongside us and then sped up again. We picked our way through the service alleys between the terraces dammed with branches and bits of bike. It felt strange seeing our house from behind as if we had crept up on it, which we had. As if we might catch it entertaining another family, which it was. As if a baby was riding around on a man's shoulders in the kitchen, which he was, as if a woman was making a large pot of coffee, which she was, as if a child sat on the floor in rapt attention rearranging the fridge magnets into a pattern that was of great significance and urgency to her and her alone.

Everything you said last night will replay on a loop for a while, but then filter into the air. You need a very tall vodka and orange. The point of taking a bath is that it's one of the few things we do deliberately – you have to really mean it. All of this is hypothetical. You could make more of an effort to protect yourself – here is a charm. Oh god no, oh god no, oh god no. Try to remember the moment you felt very afraid. Try to remember the vision. What was the vision? Everyone was having visions – it was just like the prophecy said – so it was difficult to get much attention for whatever had been visited on you; it was difficult to feel that you had any right to speak about it. You did, though, in your way. And all of the visions essentially took place in the same universe, they always did. The human hesitates and hedges because how do we know it won't set fire to the water and boil the whole sea. All of our enemies held us so close, healed our infirmities, taught us everything. The world without us always says, *Why wait?*

When I read the 'About' section about bands and fantasise about being in a band I like to fantasise about being the member of the band who, following the lead singer's side-project gaining traction, is taking indefinite time out to focus on my health. I imagine the drummer calling me one day, on my landline, and asking how I'm doing. I live in a wood-frame house and I have a small dog I take for very short walks on the beach. Mostly I wear a towel gown over my blue striped pyjamas. In the evenings I drink low-alcohol beer and wipe the table. I should probably head out and buy a bunch of cleaning products because everything is running low. *I'm good*, I say, *I'm good, Brandon, thank you for checking in, thank you for reaching out.* I'm finally reading library books. I feel tired all the time, but I sleep a lot, and the small dog gets me out every day to take the air. I eat a lot of cereal because you can get a lot of nutrients from cereal. I'll ask Brandon how things are going on the road and he'll say, *Oh, you know.*

INDEX OF FIRST LINES